cooking for two

SIMON &
SCHUSTER
ILLUSTRATED

London · New York · Sydney · Toronto

A CBS COMPANY

Nicola Graimes
Sue Ashworth

First published in Great Britain by
Simon & Schuster UK Ltd, 2011
A CBS Company

Copyright © 2011, Weight Watchers International, Inc.

SIMON AND SCHUSTER
ILLUSTRATED BOOKS
Simon & Schuster UK
222 Gray's Inn Road
London WC1X 8HB
www.simonandschuster.co.uk

Weight Watchers Publications Team: Jane Griffiths,
Cheryl Jackson, Nina McKerlie, Imogen Prescott and
Donna Watts
Simon & Schuster Project Management: WordWorks
Photography: Will Heap
Prop styling: Jenny Iggleden
Food styling: Sue Ashworth
Design and typesetting: Jane Humphrey

Recipes by Nicola Graimes:
All the recipes in *Light Meals* and *Simple Dinners* plus the
recipes on p 39, p 42 (Pork with Ginger Rhubarb Sauce),
p 47, p 50, p 51
Recipes by Sue Ashworth:
p 40, p 41, p 42 (Rich Hungarian Beef Goulash), p 44,
p 45, p 46, p 48 , p 53, p 54, p 56, p 58, p 59, p 60

Printed and bound in Singapore

A CIP catalogue for this book is available from
the British Library

Pictured on the front cover: One Pot Moroccan
Chicken, p 28

*Pictured on the back cover from left to right
and top to bottom:* Sweet Chilli Turkey Balls with
Sweetcorn Salsa, p 13; Garlic, Mushroom and Quorn
Pie, p 20; Rich Hungarian Beef Goulash, p 42; Strawberry
Soufflé Omelette, p 56.

ProPoints® value logo: You'll find this easy to read *ProPoints*
value logo on every recipe throughout this book. The logo
represents the number of *ProPoints* values per serving each recipe
contains. It is not an indication of the fillingness of a recipe.

Weight Watchers *ProPoints* Weight Loss System is a simple way to lose
weight. As part of the Weight Watchers *ProPoints* plan you'll enjoy eating
delicious, healthy, filling foods that help to keep you feeling satisfied for
longer and in control of your portions.

Filling & Healthy Foods are highlighted in green. Focus on these
foods where you can – they are healthy choices that will help you to feel
satisfied for longer.

This symbol denotes a vegetarian recipe and assumes that, where
relevant, free range eggs, vegetarian cheese, vegetarian virtually fat free
fromage frais, vegetarian low fat crème fraîche and vegetarian low fat
yogurts are used. Virtually fat free fromage frais, low fat crème fraîche and
low fat yogurts may contain traces of gelatine so they are not always
vegetarian. Please check the labels.

This symbol denotes a dish that can be frozen. Unless otherwise stated,
you can freeze the finished dish for up to 3 months. Defrost thoroughly and
reheat until the dish is piping hot throughout.

Recipe notes

Egg size Medium unless otherwise stated.

Raw eggs Only the freshest eggs should be used. Pregnant women, the
elderly and children should avoid recipes with eggs which are not fully
cooked or raw.

All fruits and vegetables Medium size unless otherwise stated.

Low fat spread Where a recipe states to use a low fat spread, a light spread
with a fat content of no less than 38% should be used.

Stock Stock cubes should be used in the recipes unless otherwise stated.

Recipe timings These are approximate and meant to be guidelines. Please
note that the preparation time includes all the steps up to and following the
main cooking time(s).

Low fat soft cheese Where a recipe states to use a low fat soft cheese, a
soft cheese with a fat content of less than 5% should be used.

Contents

Introduction

Welcome to *Cooking for Two*, the latest **ProPoints** plan cookbook from Weight Watchers, developed to work alongside the new **ProPoints** plan, our most flexible plan ever. The **ProPoints** plan has been designed to work around real life – your life – so you can keep on losing weight whatever situation you find yourself in. It is a really flexible plan and makes use of the latest research in nutritional science. The plan will help make the way you choose to eat work harder for your weight loss.

With the **ProPoints** plan, you can still eat the foods you enjoy – as you learn how to lose weight at a healthy, sustainable rate. **ProPoints** values are calculated from the protein, carbohydrate, fat and fibre content of individual foods and take into account how each of these nutrients is processed by your body and how satisfying they are.

This is the ideal cookbook for those times when you simply need a meal for two. So whether it's just the two of you or you're a couple with a young family who want to eat together after the kids have gone to bed, you'll find this book packed full of great recipe ideas. For those times when everyone is out and it's just you and your partner or another family member at home, there's plenty of inspiration with 60 recipes to choose from. You're certain to find what you need whether you're looking for a light meal, a simple supper, a special occasion dinner or a dessert. There's something to suit everyone's taste. And many of the recipes contain **Filling & Healthy Foods** that will help to keep you feeling fuller for longer and can help to S-T-R-E-T-C-H your **ProPoints** budget further.

All the recipes in *Cooking for Two* have clear step-by-step instructions and the **ProPoints** values per serving are clearly shown. With Weight Watchers and the **ProPoints** plan, you don't need to put your life on hold when you're losing weight.

These recipes are ideal for when you want something quick and delicious for lunch or supper. You're sure to turn to these fabulous, creative ideas for filling meals again and again.

Light meals

Steak sandwich with mushroom sauce

ProPoints values per recipe 22

Takes 15 mins

2 teaspoons Dijon mustard
1 tablespoon extra light mayonnaise
calorie controlled cooking spray
2 x 125 g (4½ oz) fillet steaks, visible fat removed,
    then sliced in half through the middle
200 g (7 oz) small portobello mushrooms,
    stalks trimmed and sliced
1 large garlic clove, chopped
1 tablespoon balsamic vinegar
2 tablespoons half fat crème fraîche
2 x 60 g (2 oz) baguettes, halved
1 tablespoon chopped fresh parsley
salt and freshly ground black pepper

Serve with a handful of rocket by the side, dressed in a little lemon juice, for no additional **ProPoints** values.

1 Mix together the mustard and mayonnaise. Set aside.

2 Preheat the grill to high. Heat a large non stick frying pan over a high heat. Spray the steaks with the cooking spray and cook for a minute on each side. Remove the steaks from the pan, wrap loosely in foil to keep warm and set aside.

3 Reduce the heat to medium, add the mushrooms to the pan, spray with the cooking spray and cook for 1 minute. Add the garlic and cook for another minute, stirring regularly. Pour in the balsamic vinegar and simmer for one more minute until reduced by half. Stir in the crème fraîche and 1 tablespoon of water. Heat briefly until warmed through.

4 Meanwhile, grill the baguettes on the cut sides until light golden. Spread the mustard mixture over each half. Open up the foil parcels and place one piece of steak on top of each baguette half. Pour any juice in the foil into the mushroom mixture and spoon on top of the steaks. Season and scatter over the parsley before serving two halves per person.

V **Try this** Swap the steak for 200 g (7 oz) canned chick peas, drained and rinsed, for 10 **ProPoints** values per person. Add them to the pan with the mushrooms in step 2.

7

Prawn and crab soup

ProPoints values per recipe 15

Takes 25 mins

75 g (2¾ oz) dried vermicelli noodles
calorie controlled cooking spray
2 garlic cloves, chopped
1 teaspoon chopped fresh root ginger
1 lemongrass stick, peeled and chopped finely
500 ml (18 fl oz) fish stock
1 tablespoon Thai fish sauce
juice of ½ a lime
3 tablespoons reduced fat coconut milk
4 baby corn, sliced diagonally
2 spring onions, sliced diagonally
2 tablespoons chopped fresh coriander
½ red chilli, de-seeded and chopped finely
50 g (1¾ oz) baby spinach leaves,
      stems trimmed
125 g (4½ oz) canned white crab meat in
      brine, drained
150 g (5½ oz) frozen cooked prawns
salt and freshly ground black pepper

The perfect soup for summer. Deliciously light yet rich and warming too, this main meal soup makes a great simple lunch or supper dish. Don't be put off by the length of the ingredient list – it really is very easy to make.

1 Bring a pan of water to the boil, add the noodles and cook according to the packet instructions then drain and refresh under cold running water. Drain again and set aside.

2 Heat a large non stick saucepan, spray with the cooking spray and add the garlic, ginger and lemongrass. Fry for a minute before adding the stock and fish sauce. Bring up to the boil then reduce the heat and simmer for 5 minutes.

3 Add the lime juice, coconut milk, baby corn, spring onions, half of the coriander, chilli, spinach and crab meat. Simmer over a medium-low heat for 2 minutes then add the prawns and cook for another 2 minutes.

4 Divide the noodles between two large, shallow bowls and ladle over the soup. Season and serve sprinkled with the remaining coriander.

Lamb, spinach and pasta soup

ProPoints values per recipe 20

Takes 40 mins

200 g (7 oz) lean lamb steaks, visible fat removed,
      then cut into large bite size pieces
calorie controlled cooking spray
1 onion, chopped
1 carrot, peeled and sliced
1 celery stick, sliced
300 ml (10 fl oz) hot vegetable stock
200 ml (7 fl oz) passata
1 long fresh rosemary sprig
½ teaspoon harissa paste
1 teaspoon tomato purée
75 g (2¾ oz) spinach leaves or green
      cabbage, shredded
100 g (3½ oz) dried wholewheat farfalle
salt and freshly ground black pepper
a handful of fresh basil leaves, to garnish

Hearty and filling, this is just the thing for a warming and simple meal.

1 Heat a large, lidded, non stick saucepan until hot. Spray the lamb with the cooking spray then cook for 3 minutes, turning once, until browned all over. Remove from the pan and cover with foil.

2 Add the onion, carrot and celery to the pan and spray with the cooking spray. Cook, stirring occasionally, over a medium heat for 2 minutes. Pour in the stock and passata, add the rosemary sprig, and bring up to the boil.

3 Reduce the heat, stir in the harissa paste, tomato purée and lamb then simmer, partially covered, for 15 minutes to reduce the liquid. Add the spinach or cabbage, season and cook for another 3 minutes until tender.

4 Meanwhile, bring a pan of water to the boil, add the pasta and cook, following the packet instructions, until al dente. Drain and add the pasta to the pan. Season and sprinkle with the basil leaves. Remove the rosemary sprig before serving.

Ⓥ **Try this** Try swapping the lamb for 200 g (7 oz) canned chick peas. Add with the harissa paste in step 3 for 8 **ProPoints** values per serving.

Spicy fishcakes

ProPoints values per recipe 21

Takes 35 mins

200 g (7 oz) skinless **pollock**, chopped roughly
100 g (3½ oz) frozen cooked **prawns**, defrosted
20 g (¾ oz) **fresh root ginger**, grated coarsely
1 large **garlic clove**, halved
2 **spring onions**, chopped finely
1 **egg**, beaten lightly
1 red **chilli**, de-seeded and chopped finely
    (optional)
60 g (2 oz) small **broccoli** florets
1 **carrot**, peeled, halved and cut into thin sticks
50 g (1¾ oz) **mangetout**
calorie controlled cooking spray
100 g (3½ oz) dried egg noodles

For the dressing
2 tablespoons light soy sauce
2 tablespoons sweet chilli sauce
½ teaspoon sesame oil

1 Put the pollock, prawns, ginger, garlic and spring onions in a food processor, or use a hand held blender, and whizz until finely chopped. Alternatively, chop the fish and prawns very finely then combine with the ginger, garlic, spring onions. Transfer the mixture to a mixing bowl and stir in the egg and chilli, if using.

2 Divide the mixture into four balls. Form one ball into a fishcake, flatten the top slightly and place on a plate. Repeat to make four fishcakes in total. Chill while you cook the vegetables.

3 Put the broccoli and carrot in a steamer basket, placed over a lidded pan with 2.5 cm (1 inch) boiling water. Cook for 3 minutes then add the mangetout and steam for another 2 minutes. Alternatively, add the vegetables to a pan of boiling water and cook for the same length of time then drain.

4 Meanwhile, cook the noodles according to the packet instructions then drain and return to the pan. Mix together all the ingredients for the dressing. Pour it into the pan with the noodles, add the vegetables, then turn until coated. Cover with a lid to keep warm.

5 Heat a large non stick frying pan until hot. Spritz the fishcakes with the cooking spray and cook for 5–6 minutes, turning once, until golden. Spoon the noodles on to serving plates and top with two fishcakes each.

Eggs Arnold Bennett

ProPoints values per recipe 12

Takes 20 mins

200 g (7 oz) undyed **smoked haddock**, boned
1 tablespoon half fat crème fraîche
1 tablespoon **0% fat Greek yogurt**
1 teaspoon lemon juice
½ teaspoon lemon zest
calorie controlled cooking spray
3 **eggs**, beaten lightly
1 tablespoon snipped **fresh chives**
freshly ground black pepper

1 Put the haddock in a large deep sided frying pan. Cover with hot water and poach the fish for about 6 minutes or until cooked and the fish flakes easily. Using a fish slice, transfer the haddock to a plate and leave until cool enough to handle. Remove the skin and then, using your hands, separate the fish into large flakes, taking care to remove any bones.

2 Mix together the crème fraîche, yogurt, lemon juice and zest.

3 Preheat the grill to medium-high. Heat a large, ovenproof, non stick frying pan, spray with the cooking spray, then pour in the eggs. Turn the pan until the eggs coat the base in an even layer.

4 After a few minutes and when the eggs are still slightly runny on top, arrange the haddock over the omelette then top with small spoonfuls of the crème fraîche mixture.

5 Transfer to the grill and cook for 2 minutes or until cooked through. Remove from the grill and season with black pepper. Serve half per person, sprinkled with chives.

Cook's tip If the handle of your frying pan is not ovenproof, wrap it in a double layer of foil to prevent it from burning.

Courgette, pesto and feta crostini

4 ProPoints value

ProPoints values per recipe 8

Takes 25 mins + soaking

 V

This meat-free dish can be rustled up in no time at all and makes a delicious light lunch or supper dish.

a little boiling water
25 g (1 oz) sun-dried tomatoes
1 small garlic clove
1 courgette, sliced thinly lengthways,
    outer slices discarded
calorie controlled cooking spray
1 panini (about 75 g/2¾ oz total weight),
    halved
60 g (2 oz) flame roasted red peppers in a jar,
    drained and torn into long strips
25 g (1 oz) light feta, crumbled
salt and freshly ground black pepper
a few fresh basil leaves, to garnish

1 Place the sun-dried tomatoes in a small bowl, cover with boiling water and leave to soften for 30 minutes. Drain, reserving 2 tablespoons of the soaking liquid. To make a tomato pesto, put the tomatoes in a blender, or use a hand held blender, add the reserved soaking liquid and garlic, then purée to a coarse paste. Set aside.

2 Heat a griddle pan until very hot or heat the grill to high. Spray the courgette slices with the cooking spray and then cook for 6–7 minutes, turning once. Set the courgette slices aside while you toast the panini halves for 2–4 minutes, turning once.

3 Spread the tomato pesto over the toasted bread. Top with the courgette and roasted peppers then scatter the feta and basil over the top. Season before serving.

light meals 11

Spanish egg gratin

ProPoints values per recipe 10

Takes 35 mins

200 g (7 oz) spinach, stems trimmed
calorie controlled cooking spray
1 onion, chopped
2 garlic cloves, chopped
300 ml (10 fl oz) passata
2 teaspoons tomato purée
½ teaspoon smoked paprika
1 teaspoon dried thyme
2 eggs
25 g (1 oz) half fat mature Cheddar cheese, grated
75 g (2¾ oz) baguette, split in half
1 garlic clove, halved
salt and freshly ground black pepper

1 Bring a lidded non stick saucepan of water to the boil, add the spinach and cook, covered, for about 3 minutes or until wilted. Drain well and set aside.

2 Meanwhile, heat another lidded non stick saucepan and spray with the cooking spray. Sauté the onion, covered, for 6 minutes until softened, adding a splash of water, if necessary. Add the garlic and cook for another minute.

3 Pour in the passata then stir in the tomato purée, paprika and thyme. Bring up to the boil and then reduce the heat. Cover partially then simmer for 10 minutes, stirring occasionally, until reduced and thickened.

4 Preheat the grill to medium. Spoon the spinach into a medium size baking dish. Top with the tomato sauce and make two indents in the top. Break the eggs into the indents and grill for 4 minutes until almost set. Scatter the cheese over the top and grill for a further 4–5 minutes until golden and bubbling. Season to taste.

5 Meanwhile, heat a griddle pan or non stick frying pan. Spray the bread with the cooking spray and cook for about 6 minutes, turning once, until toasted and lightly charred in places – occasionally press the bread down. Rub the top of the bread with the cut garlic and serve with the eggs.

Jacket potato with spicy lamb Bolognese

ProPoints values per recipe 23

Takes 1 hr 5 mins

 lamb Bolognese only

2 x 200 g (7 oz) baking potatoes, scrubbed
calorie controlled cooking spray
1 onion, chopped
185 g (6½ oz) lean lamb mince
2 large garlic cloves, chopped finely
1 teaspoon dried thyme
1 teaspoon ras-el-hanout
200 ml (7 fl oz) passata
100 ml (3½ fl oz) vegetable stock
25 g (1 oz) dried apricots, cut into small pieces
75 g (2¾ oz) canned cannellini beans,
    drained and rinsed
a few splashes of Tabasco (optional)
a few fresh coriander leaves
salt and freshly ground black pepper

1 Preheat the oven to Gas Mark 7/220°C/fan oven 200°C. Bake the potatoes for 1 hour until soft inside with a crisp skin outside.

2 To make the lamb Bolognese, heat a lidded non stick saucepan, spray with the cooking spray and cook the onion for 5 minutes, covered, stirring regularly, until softened. Add the lamb and cook, stirring regularly, to break up any lumps, for 5 minutes until browned all over.

3 Stir in the garlic, thyme and ras-el-hanout then add the passata, stock, apricots and cannellini beans. Bring to the boil, reduce the heat and simmer over a low heat for 15 minutes. Add a splash of Tabasco, if using, then partially cover the pan and cook for a further 15 minutes until the sauce has reduced and is thickened. Season to taste.

4 Make a cross shaped cut in the top of each baked potato and squeeze open. Spoon the lamb Bolognese on top and scatter over a few coriander leaves before serving.

Try this Use 200 g (7 oz) vegetarian mince as a replacement for the lamb for 8 **ProPoints** values per serving. You can use it from frozen – all you need to do is stir it in with the garlic in step 3.

Sweet chilli turkey balls with sweetcorn salsa

ProPoints values per recipe 16

Takes 20 mins

300 g (10½ oz) turkey mince
1 small leek, chopped finely
5 g (¼ oz) fajita spice mix
2 tablespoons chopped fresh coriander
calorie controlled cooking spray
2 tablespoons sweet chilli sauce
salt and freshly ground black pepper

For the sweetcorn salsa
100 g (3½ oz) canned sweetcorn, drained
1 tomato, de-seeded and diced
25 g (1 oz) jalapeño chillies from a jar, drained
    and chopped roughly
½ small red onion, diced
juice of ½ a lime

Serve these sweet chilli glazed meatballs on top of one warmed Weight Watchers wholemeal pitta bread per person, and with a handful of watercress on the side, for an extra 3 **ProPoints** values per person.

1 Preheat the grill to medium-high and line a baking tray with foil. To make the turkey balls, mix together the turkey mince, leek, fajita spice mix and coriander. Season, then using wet hands, form the turkey mixture into 12 walnut sized balls.

2 Spray the turkey balls with the cooking spray and grill for 8 minutes, turning occasionally. Brush the top of the balls with half of the sweet chilli sauce and grill for another minute, then turn them over. Brush with the remaining sweet chilli sauce and grill for 1 minute until glossy and golden.

3 Meanwhile, prepare the salsa by combining all the ingredients in a bowl. Season then serve alongside the turkey balls.

Try this Make it with the same quantity of lean pork mince instead of turkey mince, for the same **ProPoints** values per person.

Light meals 13

Seared chicken with mint yogurt dressing

ProPoints values per recipe 18

Takes 25 mins

75 g (2¾ oz) dried **wholewheat couscous**
½ a kettleful of boiling water
½ teaspoon vegetable stock powder or ½ a stock cube
300 g (10½ oz) **skinless boneless chicken breast**, cut into 1 cm (½ inch) wide strips
2 teaspoons dried thyme
2 teaspoons ground coriander
calorie controlled cooking spray
50 g (1¾ oz) frozen **peas**
50 g (1¾ oz) **sugar snap peas**, sliced diagonally
½ red **pepper**, de-seeded and cut into thin strips
1 large **spring onion**, sliced diagonally
salt and freshly ground black pepper

For the mint yogurt dressing
a small handful of **fresh mint** leaves
75 g (2¾ oz) **0% fat Greek yogurt**
juice of ½ a lime
½ teaspoon cumin seeds

1 Put the couscous in a bowl, pour over enough boiling water to cover, stir in the stock powder and cover with a plate. Leave for about 5 minutes or until the stock is absorbed and the grains are tender. Using a fork, fluff up the couscous and set aside.

2 Meanwhile, using a hand held blender, blend together all the dressing ingredients, except the cumin seeds. If you don't have a hand held blender, finely chop the mint and combine with the remaining ingredients. Transfer to a bowl, season and scatter over the cumin seeds.

3 Sprinkle the chicken with the thyme and coriander. Season then turn until evenly coated. Heat a griddle pan or non stick frying pan over a high heat. Spray the chicken with the cooking spray. Cook over a medium-high heat for 6 minutes, turning once, until cooked through and golden.

4 Meanwhile, bring a saucepan of water to the boil, add the peas, sugar snap peas, pepper and spring onion and cook for 3 minutes or until tender. Drain and refresh under cold running water.

5 To serve, divide the couscous between two large, shallow bowls then top with the peas, sugar snap peas, red pepper, spring onion and chicken. Spoon over the dressing before serving.

Ⓥ Try this Swap the chicken for 2 x 15 g (½ oz) slices of light halloumi per person for 8 **ProPoints** values per serving. Pat dry with kitchen towel and prepare in the same way as the chicken in step 3, then griddle or pan fry for 2 minutes on each side or until golden.

Parma ham and pear salad

ProPoints values per recipe 8

Takes 10 mins

4 slices Parma ham
1 slice of wholemeal bread, crusts removed
1 **garlic clove**, halved
50 g (1¾ oz) **spinach**, **rocket** and **watercress** salad
1 **pear**, peeled, cored and sliced lengthways

For the dressing
1 heaped teaspoon wholegrain mustard
1 teaspoon clear honey
1 tablespoon lemon juice
1 teaspoon extra virgin olive oil
salt and freshly ground black pepper

1 Preheat the grill to medium-high and line the grill pan with foil. Grill the Parma ham for 3–4 minutes, turning once, until crisp. Pat dry with kitchen paper and set aside.

2 Meanwhile, to make the dressing, mix together all the ingredients in a small bowl then season to taste.

3 Grill both sides of the bread until toasted. Rub the cut side of the garlic over both sides of the warm toasted bread then leave to cool. When cool, cut into small, bite size cubes and set aside.

4 Divide the salad leaves between two plates, top with the pear then spoon over the dressing. Scatter over the croutons and place two slices of Parma ham on top of each serving.

Ⓥ Try this Swap the Parma ham for 4 x 14 g (½ oz) vegetarian bacon rashers for the same **ProPoints** values per person. Grill for 5 minutes until slightly crisp.

Italian beef burgers

ProPoints values per recipe 19

Takes 15 minutes

 uncooked burgers only

200 g (7 oz) lean beef mince
2 teaspoons red pesto
1 large **garlic clove**, minced
calorie controlled cooking spray
2 mini pitta breads (round ones), about
    45 g (1½ oz) each
40 g (1½ oz) mozzarella light, sliced into
    four pieces
1 **tomato**, sliced
4 large **fresh basil leaves**
salt and freshly ground black pepper

Pesto, mozzarella and basil give these tasty burgers a delicious Italian twist. Serve with sliced red **pepper**, **cucumber**, **celery** and **carrot** sticks for no additional **ProPoints** values.

1 Put the mince in a bowl with the pesto and garlic then season. Stir with a fork to break up the mince and make sure everything is thoroughly combined. Using your hands, form the mixture into two burgers.

2 Heat a non stick frying pan over a high heat until hot, then reduce the heat to medium. Spray the burgers with cooking spray then cook for 6–8 minutes, turning every 2 minutes, until golden and cooked through. (If you prefer your burger rare, cook for about 5–6 minutes.)

3 Meanwhile, warm the pitta breads in a toaster on a low heat. Split open the pittas and top with the burger, mozzarella, tomato and basil. Cover with the top of the pitta and serve immediately.

Cook's tip If preferred, grill the burgers under a high grill for the same length of time, turning occasionally. The pitta breads can also be warmed under the grill for a minute on each side.

Quorn toasties

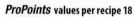

ProPoints values per recipe 18

Takes 20 mins

2 **courgettes**, sliced thinly lengthways,
    outer slices discarded
calorie controlled cooking spray
2 teaspoons lemon juice
1 tablespoon chopped **fresh mint**
4 x 51 g (1¾ oz) **Quorn fillets**, defrosted
    and sliced lengthways
12 g (½ oz) fajita spice mix
2 Weight Watchers bagels, halved
4 tablespoons reduced fat guacamole
½ small red **pepper**, de-seeded and diced
1 teaspoon chopped **fresh coriander** (optional)
salt and freshly ground black pepper

This open sandwich has some delicious Mexican ingredients: creamy guacamole, fajita spices and **fresh coriander**.

1 Heat a griddle or non stick frying pan over a high heat. Spray the courgettes with the cooking spray and cook over a medium-high heat for 6–8 minutes, turning once, until tender and charred in places. Transfer to a dish, season, then sprinkle over the lemon juice and mint. Set aside until ready to serve.

2 Toss the Quorn fillets in the fajita spice mix until evenly coated. Return the griddle or non stick frying pan to a medium-high heat. Spray the Quorn with the cooking spray and cook for 6 minutes, turning once, or until light golden and cooked through. Meanwhile, lightly toast the bagel.

3 Spread a tablespoon of guacamole over each bagel half, top with the red pepper and Quorn. Season and scatter over the lime juice and coriander, if using, before serving with the mint courgettes by the side.

Try this You could use 275 g (9½ oz) **mini chicken fillets** instead of the Quorn. Prepare in the same way as the Quorn and cook for 8 minutes, turning once, or until cooked through, for 10 **ProPoints** values per serving.

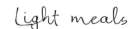

Crispy bacon and bean sauté

ProPoints values per recipe 14

Takes 20 mins

calorie controlled cooking spray
125 g (4½ oz) lean back bacon, trimmed of fat,
    and chopped roughly
2 **garlic cloves**, chopped
125 g (4½ oz) **Savoy cabbage** or **curly kale**,
    shredded finely
10 **cherry tomatoes**, halved
400 g can **butterbeans**, drained and rinsed
½ teaspoon dried chilli flakes
1 tablespoon lemon juice
1 tablespoon half fat crème fraîche
salt and freshly ground black pepper

This one pot meal takes just minutes to make and goes well with a medium slice of crusty bread per person, for an extra 2 **ProPoints** values per serving.

1 Heat a non stick frying pan, spray with the cooking spray and cook the bacon, stirring regularly, for 5 minutes until golden and slightly crisp.

2 Add the garlic and cabbage, or kale, spray with the cooking spray, and stir fry for 2 minutes.

3 Next, add the tomatoes, butterbeans and chilli flakes and cook for 2 minutes before stirring in the lemon juice, 1 tablespoon of hot water and the crème fraîche. Warm through for 1 minute, stirring. Season and serve.

V Try this For a vegetarian alternative, swap the bacon for 150 g (5½ oz) **Quorn Chicken Style Pieces** for 6 **ProPoints** values per person. Cook in the same way as the bacon.

Light meals

After a long day, sitting down to enjoy a tasty dinner together is a great way to relax. You'll love these easy recipes – they're full of exciting flavours and textures and will leave you feeling satisfied.

Simple dinners

Japanese pork with chilli glaze

ProPoints values per recipe 11

Takes 40 mins + 1 hr marinating

300 g (10½ oz) **lean pork tenderloin**,
   trimmed of visible fat
6 small **broccoli** florets
calorie controlled cooking spray
1 large **garlic clove**, sliced thinly
1 cm (½ inch) piece **fresh root ginger**, grated
1 **pak choi**, sliced
2 **spring onions**, sliced diagonally
60 g (2 oz) **sugar snap peas**

For the marinade
1 tablespoon miso paste
3 tablespoons light soy sauce or tamari
a good pinch of dried chilli flakes
1 teaspoon caster sugar

The pork has a wonderful sticky glaze and comes with a crisp vegetable stir fry. Serve with 50 g (1¾ oz) dried wholewheat noodles per person, for an extra 4 *ProPoints* values per serving.

1 To make the marinade, mix together all the ingredients in a shallow dish, add the pork and turn until coated. Cover and leave to marinate in the fridge for up to 1 hour. Preheat the oven to Gas Mark 5/190°C/fan oven 170°C.

2 Meanwhile, bring a pan of water to the boil, add the broccoli and blanch for 2 minutes then drain and refresh under cold running water.

3 Wrap the pork in foil, place on a baking tray then roast for 15 minutes. Preheat the grill to high.

4 Open the foil parcel, spoon the marinade over the pork and place under the grill for 3 minutes, turning once, until golden and glazed. Leave to rest while you make the vegetable stir fry.

5 Heat a wok or non stick frying pan, spray with the cooking spray and stir fry the garlic, ginger, pak choi, spring onions, sugar snap peas and broccoli for 3 minutes, adding a splash of water, if they start to stick.

6 Slice the pork into 1 cm (½ inch) thick rounds and serve with the vegetables, spooning any juices from the pork over the top.

Garlic, mushroom and Quorn pies

ProPoints values per recipe 15

20 mins prep, 30 mins cooking

 filling only

calorie controlled cooking spray
1 leek, sliced
150 g (5½ oz) chestnut mushrooms, sliced
2 garlic cloves, chopped finely
2 teaspoons fresh thyme leaves or
   1 teaspoon dried thyme
200 g (7 oz) Quorn Chicken Style Pieces
75 g (2¾ oz) frozen petit pois
60 g (2 oz) low fat soft cheese with garlic and herbs
100 ml (3½ fl oz) skimmed milk
2 x 45 g (1½ oz) filo sheets, measuring 50 x 24 cm
   (20 x 9½ inches), and defrosted if frozen
salt and freshly ground black pepper

1 Preheat the oven to Gas Mark 6/200°C/fan oven 180°C. Heat a medium size, non stick saucepan and spray with the cooking spray. Add the leek, mushrooms and garlic and cook for 2 minutes, stirring regularly. Stir in the thyme, Quorn and peas. Cook, stirring, for another 3 minutes.

2 Add the soft cheese and milk, season, and cook for a minute until hot. Spoon the mixture into two 250 ml (9 fl oz) pie dishes.

3 Scrunch up each sheet of filo pastry and then place on top of the pies to fit the dishes. Spray the top of the pies with the cooking spray, place on a baking sheet, and bake for 25–30 minutes until golden.

Try this Replace the Quorn with the same weight of cubed skinless boneless chicken breast. Spray a non stick frying pan with cooking spray and then cook the chicken for 5 minutes. Continue, following the instructions in step 1. The **ProPoints** values per serving will be the same.

 Cook's tip To freeze, transfer the filling to a freezerproof container at the end of step 2. Defrost thoroughly before use and follow the recipe from step 3.

Winter ratatouille

ProPoints values per recipe 16

10 mins prep, 1 hr cooking

 ratatouille only

300 g (10½ oz) butternut squash,
   peeled, de-seeded and cubed
6 shallots, peeled and halved, if large
1 carrot, peeled and cubed
1 turnip, peeled and cubed
2 parsnips, peeled and cubed
calorie controlled cooking spray
4 large sprigs of fresh thyme
1 leek, cut into 2.5 cm (1 inch) slices
400 g can cherry tomatoes
1 tablespoon balsamic vinegar
1 tablespoon dark soy sauce
a few splashes of Tabasco
100 g (3½ oz) mozzarella light
85 g (3 oz) dried bulgur wheat
salt and freshly ground black pepper

1 Preheat the oven to Gas Mark 6/200°C/fan oven 180°C. Put the squash, shallots, carrot, turnip and parsnips in a large, deep roasting tin. Spray with the cooking spray, scatter the thyme over the top and roast for 30 minutes.

2 Carefully remove the tin from the oven and add the leek. Pour over the cherry tomatoes, balsamic vinegar, soy sauce and Tabasco then stir until combined and the vegetables are evenly spread in the tin. Season, cover with foil and roast for another 20 minutes. Remove the foil, scatter over the mozzarella and cook for 10 minutes until melted.

3 Meanwhile, put the bulgur wheat in a lidded saucepan, just cover with water, and bring to the boil. Reduce the heat to low, cover, and simmer for 5 minutes or until tender and the water has been absorbed. Using a fork, fluff up the grains and divide between two large, shallow bowls. Top with the ratatouille, removing the thyme sprigs, and then serve.

 Cook's tip To freeze, transfer to a freezerproof container after step 2.

Cantonese orange duck

ProPoints values per recipe 11

Takes 25 mins

1 tablespoon sweet chilli sauce
6 tablespoons fresh orange juice
1 tablespoon light soy sauce
240 g (8½ oz) skinless duck breast, cut into
    1 cm (½ inch) slices
calorie controlled cooking spray
2 spring onions, sliced diagonally
2 cm (¾ inch) fresh root ginger,
    sliced into thin rounds
½ teaspoon Chinese five spice
1 small orange, peeled and cut into thin rounds
salt and freshly ground black pepper

If you like spice, add a pinch of chilli flakes in step 3 with the soy sauce. This dish is delicious with 50 g (1¾ oz) dried brown basmati rice per person, cooked according to the packet instructions, for an extra 5 **ProPoints** values per serving.

1️⃣ Mix together the sweet chilli sauce, orange juice and soy sauce.
2️⃣ Heat a wok or non stick frying pan. Spray the duck with the cooking spray then stir fry for 3 minutes. Add the white part of the spring onions and ginger then stir fry for another 2 minutes.
3️⃣ Add the soy sauce mixture to the pan with the Chinese five spice and stir fry for 2 minutes. Add the orange and cook for 1 more minute until reduced and thickened. Season and scatter over the green part of the spring onion before serving.

Try this Swap the duck for 250 g (9 oz) lean pork strips and cook for the same length of time. The **ProPoints** values will be 6 per serving.

Slow cooked Asian beef stew

ProPoints values per recipe 11

30 mins prep, 1 hr cooking

calorie controlled cooking spray
250 g (9 oz) lean stewing beef, visible fat
    removed, and cut into 2.5 cm (1 inch) pieces
1 onion, sliced
2 garlic cloves, sliced
2.5 cm (1 inch) piece fresh root ginger, grated
3 cardamom pods, split
2 lemongrass sticks, peeled and chopped finely
300 ml (10 fl oz) vegetable stock
2 teaspoons massaman curry paste
1 large carrot, peeled and sliced thickly
3 tablespoons reduced fat coconut milk
finely grated zest and juice of a lime
salt and freshly ground black pepper

The beauty of a stew is that the taste improves with time, so this Asian inspired dinner is ideal for making the day before, if preferred. Serve with 50 g (1¾ oz) dried Thai jasmine rice, cooked according to packet instructions, per person for an extra 5 **ProPoints** values per serving.

1️⃣ Heat a large, lidded, flameproof casserole dish and spray with the cooking spray. Add the beef and cook for about 5 minutes until browned all over. Remove the beef, cover with foil and set aside.
2️⃣ Add the onion to the dish, spray with the cooking spray and sauté, covered, stirring occasionally, for 5 minutes. Stir in the garlic, ginger, cardamom and lemongrass then pour in the stock. Bring up to the boil, then reduce the heat and stir in the massaman curry paste.
3️⃣ Return the beef to the dish with the carrot then simmer, covered, for 45 minutes. Add the coconut milk, lime zest and juice. Season and simmer, covered, for a further 15 minutes. Remove the lid and simmer for a few minutes to reduce the sauce, if necessary. Serve immediately.

Cook's tip You'll find the massaman curry paste in the Asian or specialist section in major supermarkets or oriental food stores.

Herb rubbed steak with squash mash

ProPoints values per recipe 11

Takes 35 mins

calorie controlled cooking spray

1 red **onion**, sliced

1 tablespoon balsamic vinegar

3 large **fresh thyme sprigs**, plus 1 tablespoon
    fresh thyme leaves

1 large **garlic clove**, halved

2 x 140 g (5 oz) **lean beef fillet steaks**,
    visible fat removed

For the squash mash

600 g (1 lb 5 oz) **butternut squash**, peeled,
    de-seeded and cut into bite size pieces

1 **garlic clove**, halved

1 tablespoon light mayonnaise

salt and freshly ground black pepper

This simple meal makes a great weekend supper. Serve with **spinach**, cooked in a little water until tender and then drained, for no additional **ProPoints** values.

1 Heat a lidded non stick saucepan, spray with the cooking spray and cook the onion over a low heat, covered, for 15 minutes until very soft. Stir occasionally and add a splash of water if the onion starts to stick. Add the balsamic vinegar and the tablespoon of thyme leaves. Stir then add 5 tablespoons of water. Cook, uncovered, for 2 minutes until reduced by half. Cover to keep warm and set aside.

2 Meanwhile, bring a pan of water to the boil, add the squash and garlic and cook for 15 minutes or until tender. Drain well, add the mayonnaise and mash until smooth. Season and set aside, covered, to keep warm.

3 Rub both sides of each steak with the thyme sprigs and the cut side of the garlic. Season and spray with the cooking spray. When the onion gravy and mash are ready, heat a griddle pan or non stick frying pan until very hot, add the steaks and cook for 1–1½ minutes on each side or until cooked to your liking.

4 To serve, put a steak on each serving plate. Pour any juices in the pan into the onion gravy then spoon the gravy over the top. Spoon the mash by the side.

Pasta with feta and mint

ProPoints values per recipe 18

Takes 25 mins

125 g (4½ oz) dried linguine

1 **courgette**, grated

1 **leek**, sliced thinly

75 g (2¾ oz) frozen **petit pois**

1 teaspoon olive oil

2 **garlic cloves**, crushed

1 tablespoon lemon juice

4 tablespoons chopped **fresh mint**

75 g (2¾ oz) reduced fat feta, cubed

salt and freshly ground black pepper

A delightfully summery pasta dish.

1 Bring a large pan of water to the boil, add the pasta and cook according to the packet instructions, then add the courgette, leek and peas a minute before the end of the cooking time. Drain the pasta and vegetables, reserving 6 tablespoons of the cooking water.

2 Heat a large non stick frying pan, spray with the cooking spray, add the olive oil and garlic and cook for 1 minute until softened. Add the pasta, vegetables and reserved cooking water then stir until warmed through.

3 Remove from the heat and stir in the lemon juice, mint and feta cheese. Season, toss until combined and then serve.

Try this Instead of the feta, add 250 g (9 oz) **skinless boneless chicken breasts**, cut into bite size pieces. Cook in a non stick frying pan, sprayed with cooking spray, for 6–8 minutes until golden and cooked through then continue with the recipe in step 2, for 10 **ProPoints** values per serving.

Vegetable pilaf with spiced cashews

ProPoints values per recipe 16

10 mins prep, 25 mins cooking

calorie controlled cooking spray
1 teaspoon cumin seeds
5 cardamom pods, split open
100 g (3½ oz) dried **brown basmati rice**
225 ml (8 fl oz) vegetable stock
100 g (3½ oz) **spinach leaves**
1 teaspoon turmeric
1 teaspoon low fat spread
4 **spring onions**, trimmed and cut into four
½ red **pepper**, de-seeded and sliced lengthways
100 g (3½ oz) **fennel**, cut into thin slices
25 g (1 oz) cashews
¼ teaspoon smoked paprika
freshly ground black pepper

1 Heat a lidded saucepan, spray with the cooking spray and toast the cumin seeds for 1 minute then add the cardamom, rice and stock. Stir and bring up to the boil. Reduce the heat to its lowest setting, cover, and simmer for 20 minutes. Stir in the spinach and cook for another 2 minutes until the water has been absorbed and the rice and spinach are tender.

2 Remove the pan from the heat. Season with pepper, stir in the turmeric and low fat spread then cover and set aside for 5 minutes.

3 About 10 minutes before the rice is ready, spray the spring onions, red pepper and fennel with the cooking spray. Heat a griddle pan or non stick frying pan over a high heat then cook the vegetables for 8–10 minutes, turning once, until tender and charred in places.

4 Meanwhile, dry fry the cashews in a non stick frying pan for 3–5 minutes until golden. Transfer the nuts to a bowl, spray with the cooking spray and toss in the smoked paprika. Set aside.

5 To serve, remove the cardamom pods from the rice and divide the rice between two plates. Top with the vegetables and scatter over the cashews.

Try this Instead of the cashews, top each plate with half a boiled **egg** for 7 **ProPoints** values per serving.

Quick lamb and chick pea hot pot

ProPoints values per recipe 18

Takes 35 mins

calorie controlled cooking spray
1 red or white onion, chopped
1 large carrot, peeled and sliced thickly
1 parsnip, peeled and cut into 1 cm (½ inch) cubes
1 leek, sliced thickly
1 celery stick, sliced
2 bay leaves
1 long fresh rosemary sprig, plus two extra
    to garnish
400 ml (14 fl oz) vegetable stock
60 g (2 oz) canned chick peas, drained and rinsed
1 teaspoon half fat crème fraîche
1 teaspoon Dijon mustard
2 x 125 g (4½ oz) lean lamb steaks, trimmed of fat
salt and freshly ground black pepper

1 Heat a lidded flameproof casserole dish and spray with the cooking spray. Add the onion and sauté, covered, for 5 minutes. Add the carrot, parsnip, leek and celery. Stir, then cover and cook for another 5 minutes, until softened.

2 Add the bay leaves, rosemary, stock and chick peas and then bring to the boil. Reduce the heat, cover partially, and simmer until the vegetables are tender. Stir in the crème fraîche and mustard. Season and warm through.

3 Meanwhile, preheat the grill to high and line the grill pan with foil. Alternatively, heat a griddle pan until hot. Spray the lamb with the cooking spray and season. Grill or griddle for 3 minutes on each side or until cooked to your liking.

4 Remove the rosemary. Ladle the vegetables and stock into large, shallow bowls, top with the lamb steaks and a sprig of rosemary.

Try this Serve with a teaspoon of mint sauce per serving, if you wish, for no additional **ProPoints** values.

One pot Moroccan chicken

ProPoints values per recipe 28

30 mins prep, 25 mins cooking

325 g (11½ oz) skinless boneless chicken thighs
calorie controlled cooking spray
1 large **onion**, chopped
½ pointed red **pepper**, de-seeded and
    sliced into thin rings
2 **garlic cloves**, chopped
1 teaspoon ras-el-hanout
1 teaspoon ground coriander
1 teaspoon dried thyme
100 g (3½ oz) dried **brown basmati rice**
150 ml (5 fl oz) unsweetened orange juice
100 ml (3½ fl oz) vegetable stock
50 g (1¾ oz) fresh **mango**, sliced thinly
3 **fresh coriander sprigs**, leaves removed
salt and freshly ground black pepper

1 Spray the chicken with the cooking spray. Heat a lidded flameproof casserole dish or heavy based saucepan over a medium heat then brown for 3 minutes on each side until golden. Remove from the pan and set aside, covered.

2 Spray the casserole dish with the cooking spray. Add the onion then cover and cook for 6 minutes, stirring occasionally, and adding a splash of water if the onion starts to stick. When the onion has softened, stir in the red pepper, garlic, ras-el-hanout, ground coriander, thyme and rice. Cook for 2 minutes until the rice is opaque.

3 Pour in the orange juice and stock, stir and then bring to the boil. Place the chicken on top of the rice and reduce the heat to the lowest setting. Cover and cook for 20–25 minutes or until the rice is tender and the chicken is cooked through.

4 Divide the rice and chicken between two serving plates. Season to taste and then scatter the mango and fresh coriander over the top.

Cook's tip If freezing, transfer to a freezerproof container. Before serving, defrost thoroughly and then put in a lidded flameproof casserole dish. Add a splash of water to prevent the rice from sticking then cover and reheat over a medium-low heat until piping hot.

Chilli chicken

ProPoints values per recipe 11

Takes 30 mins + 30 mins marinating

2 x 165 g (5¾ oz) **skinless boneless
    chicken breasts**
2 tablespoons sweet chilli sauce
2 tablespoons light soy sauce
2.5 cm (1 inch) **fresh root ginger**, grated
calorie controlled cooking spray
50 g (1¾ oz) **red cabbage**, shredded
50 g (1¾ oz) **white cabbage**, shredded
1 **carrot**, peeled and grated
1 **spring onion**, chopped finely
2 tablespoons Thai fish sauce
juice of ½ a lime
1 teaspoon caster sugar
salt and freshly ground black pepper

1 Put the chicken between two sheets of cling film and, using the end of a rolling pin or meat mallet, flatten it until about 1.5 cm (⅝ inch) thick.

2 Mix together the sweet chilli sauce and soy sauce in a large, shallow dish. Using your hand, squeeze the juice from the ginger into the bowl, season and then add the chicken. Turn to coat in the marinade then cover and leave in the fridge for at least 30 minutes.

3 Meanwhile, put the red and white cabbage, carrot and spring onion in a serving bowl. Mix together the fish sauce, lime juice and sugar, until the latter has dissolved, and then pour it over the vegetables. Season and toss until coated in the dressing.

4 Heat a non stick frying pan until hot. Spray the chicken with the cooking spray and cook over a medium heat for 8–10 minutes, turning once until cooked through. Serve the chicken with the cabbage.

Try this This dish works particularly well with fish. Swap the chicken for 2 x 175 g (6 oz) thick fillets of **pollock** and prepare and cook in the same way. The **ProPoints** values will be 5 per serving.

Spiced lentils with lamb

ProPoints values per recipe 19

Takes 35 mins

calorie controlled cooking spray
1 large **onion**, chopped
2 **garlic cloves**, chopped
1 teaspoon cumin seeds
1 **carrot**, peeled and sliced
1 teaspoon ground coriander
½ teaspoon smoked paprika
200 g (7 oz) canned green **lentils**, drained
    and rinsed (drained weight)
200 g (7 oz) canned **tomatoes**
100 ml (3½ fl oz) vegetable stock
100 g (3½ oz) baby **spinach leaves**
2 x 125 g (4½ oz) lean lamb steaks, trimmed of fat
1 tablespoon chopped **fresh coriander** (optional)
salt and freshly ground black pepper

1 Spray a large, lidded, non stick saucepan with the cooking spray. Cover and cook the onion for 6 minutes, stirring occasionally. Add a splash of water if the onions start to stick. Add the garlic and cumin, spray again with the cooking spray and cook for another minute.

2 Meanwhile, bring a pan of water to the boil. Add the carrots and cook for 4–5 minutes until just tender. Drain and set aside.

3 Stir the ground coriander, smoked paprika, green lentils, tomatoes and stock into the onions. Bring to the boil then reduce the heat and simmer for 10 minutes until reduced and thickened. Add the spinach to the pan. Cover and cook for about 2 minutes until wilted then stir in the carrot. Season to taste.

4 Just before the lentils are ready, spray the lamb with the cooking spray. Heat a non stick frying pan until hot, add the lamb and cook for 2–3 minutes on each side or until cooked to your liking.

5 Divide the lentil mixture between two serving plates, top with the lamb then scatter over the coriander, if using, before serving.

V Try this For a vegetarian dish, why not top the spiced lentils with one poached **egg** per person instead of the lamb, for 6 **ProPoints** values per serving.

Beef and vegetable noodle bowl

ProPoints values per recipe 24

Takes 25 mins

225 g (8 oz) **lean beef fillet**, cut into strips
1 tablespoon hoisin sauce
60 g (2 oz) small **broccoli** florets
1 **carrot**, peeled and cut into thirds, then julienned
100 g (3½ oz) fine egg noodles
calorie controlled cooking spray
50 g (1¾ oz) **sugar snap peas**
25 g (1 oz) **fresh root ginger**, chopped finely
1 large **spring onion**, sliced diagonally
¼ red **chilli**, de-seeded and sliced thinly
600 ml (20 fl oz) vegetable stock
2 tablespoons miso paste
1 tablespoon dark soy sauce
15 g (½ oz) **beansprouts**
1 tablespoon chopped **fresh coriander**

1 Put the beef in a dish, spoon over the hoisin sauce, then turn to coat.

2 Bring a pan of water to the boil, add the broccoli and carrot, cook for 2 minutes then add the noodles. Return to the boil and cook for another 2–3 minutes until tender. Drain and refresh under cold water. Set aside.

3 Heat a wok or large non stick frying pan. Add the beef (discarding any remaining hoisin sauce in the bowl) and spray with the cooking spray. Stir fry for 2 minutes then remove from the pan and set aside.

4 Wipe the pan with kitchen paper, spray again with cooking spray and stir fry the sugar snap peas, ginger, spring onion and chilli for 2 minutes.

5 Meanwhile, heat the stock in a saucepan then stir in the miso paste and soy sauce until dissolved.

6 Divide the noodles, beef and vegetables between two large serving bowls. Pour over the stock then sprinkle over the beansprouts and coriander.

V Try this You could swap the beef for the same weight of marinated **tofu** pieces for 14 **ProPoints** values per serving. Omit the hoisin sauce and stir fry as in step 3 for 2 minutes.

Penne pasta with prawns and basil

9 ProPoints value

ProPoints values per recipe 18

Takes 20 mins

125 g (4½ oz) dried penne
2 courgettes, quartered lengthways
 and sliced into chunks
calorie controlled cooking spray
1 teaspoon olive oil
3 garlic cloves, crushed
1 red chilli, de-seeded and sliced thinly
200 g (7 oz) frozen raw king prawns, defrosted
1 tablespoon lemon juice
a handful of fresh basil leaves, torn
salt and freshly ground black pepper

1 Bring a pan of water to the boil, add the pasta and cook according to the packet instructions. Two minutes before the end of the cooking time, add the courgettes, return to the boil and cook until tender. Drain, reserving 3 tablespoons of the cooking water.

2 Meanwhile, heat a large non stick frying pan. Spray with the cooking spray then add the oil, garlic, chilli and prawns and fry for 3 minutes, stirring regularly until the prawns are pink.

3 Add the pasta, courgettes, cooking water and lemon juice to the prawns and warm through for 1 minute. Season and divide between two plates. Scatter over the basil.

Try this Instead of raw prawns, use ready cooked ones. Toss in at the end in step 3.

V For a vegetarian alternative, swap the prawns for 150 g (5½ oz) canned chick peas, drained and rinsed. Add them to the pan with the garlic in step 2 for the same **ProPoints** values.

Summer white bean and vegetable stew

ProPoints values per recipe 19

Takes 40 mins

calorie controlled cooking spray
1 red **onion**, sliced
2 **garlic cloves**, sliced
1 small red **pepper**, de-seeded and sliced
1 **corn on the cob**, kernels removed
150 ml (5 fl oz) dry white wine
1 tablespoon cornflour
100 g (3½ oz) fine **green beans**, halved
2 large sprigs of **fresh thyme**
200 g (7 oz) canned **cannellini beans**,
    drained and rinsed
300 ml (10 fl oz) vegetable stock
100 g (3½ oz) baby leaf **spinach**
2 tablespoons reduced fat houmous
finely grated zest of 1 lemon
salt and freshly ground black pepper
a small handful of **fresh basil leaves**,
    to garnish (optional)

This light yet filling vegetarian stew is a lovely meal-in-one.

1 Heat a large, lidded, heavy based saucepan and spray with the cooking spray. Add the onion then cover and cook for 6 minutes until softened. Add the garlic, red pepper and corn and cook for another minute before pouring in the wine. Bring up to the boil then reduce the heat to low and simmer for about 5 minutes or until the wine has reduced by half.

2 Mix the cornflour with a little water to make a paste. Add to the pan and cook, stirring, for a minute until thickened then add the green beans, thyme, cannellini beans and stock and return to the boil. Reduce the heat to low and simmer for about 8 minutes until the vegetables are tender. Add the spinach and cook, partially covered, until wilted.

3 Divide between two large, shallow bowls. Season to taste and top each portion with 1 tablespoon of houmous. Sprinkle with black pepper and lemon zest before serving. If using, garnish with basil leaves too.

Try this Instead of fresh corn, you could also use 100 g (3½ oz) canned or frozen **sweetcorn**.

Sausage and pear hot pot

ProPoints values per recipe 12

25 mins prep, 20 mins cooking

calorie controlled cooking spray
4 reduced fat Cumberland sausages,
    each sliced into four
1 large **onion**, sliced
2 **garlic cloves**, chopped
1 teaspoon dried thyme
½ teaspoon fennel seeds
225 g (8 oz) **butternut squash**, peeled,
    de-seeded and cut into bite size pieces
1 tablespoon plain flour
400 ml (14 fl oz) vegetable stock
1 **pear**, cored and cut into bite size pieces
1 tablespoon wholegrain mustard
salt and freshly ground black pepper

For the perfect mashed potato, boil 100 g (3½ oz) cubed **potatoes** per person until tender then mash with 1 tablespoon each of light mayonnaise and skimmed milk per person, for 4 **ProPoints** values per serving.

1 Heat a large non stick saucepan over a medium heat then spray with the cooking spray. Add the sausages and cook for 6 minutes, turning occasionally, until browned. Remove from the pan, cover, and set aside.

2 Add the onion to the pan, spray with the cooking spray and cook for 6 minutes, covered, until softened. Add the garlic, thyme, fennel seeds and squash. Cook, stirring, for another minute.

3 Add the flour and cook, stirring continuously, for a further minute. Pour in the stock and bring to the boil then reduce the heat. Add the pear and simmer over a low heat, stirring occasionally, for 20 minutes until the stock has reduced and the squash is tender. Season and stir in the mustard.

V Try this Use the same quantity of Cumberland Quorn sausages for 5 **ProPoints** values per serving. Prepare and cook them as described above.

Pork with quick beetroot and apple chutney

ProPoints values per recipe 18

Takes 50 mins

calorie controlled cooking spray
250 g (9 oz) **pork tenderloin**
275 g (9½ oz) **parsnips**, peeled and quartered
    lengthways
salt and freshly ground black pepper

For the beetroot and apple chutney
140 g (5 oz) raw **beetroot**, peeled and grated
2 **apples**, cored and grated
1 small **onion**, grated
2.5 cm (1 inch) **fresh root ginger**, grated
1 **garlic clove**, chopped
150 ml (5 fl oz) unsweetened orange juice
3 tablespoons cider vinegar
2 tablespoons caster sugar

1 Preheat the oven to Gas Mark 6/200°C/fan oven 180°C. To make the chutney, put all the ingredients in a saucepan, bring to the boil then reduce the heat to low and simmer, stirring occasionally, for 25 minutes until the liquid has reduced. It should be thick but remain a little juicy.

2 Meanwhile, spray a large non stick roasting tin with the cooking spray. Arrange the parsnips in an even layer, spray with the cooking spray and roast for 15 minutes.

3 While the parsnips are roasting, heat a non stick frying pan over a medium-high heat. Spray the pork with the cooking spray and brown in the pan for 5 minutes, turning occasionally, until golden all over.

4 Remove the roasting tin from the oven, turn the parsnips over and move them to the edges of the tin, then spray with the cooking spray. Place the pork in the centre and roast for 15 minutes or until cooked. Remove the pork from the oven, wrap loosely with foil, and then leave to rest for 5 minutes. Meanwhile, roast the parsnips for another 5 minutes.

5 To serve, spoon 75 g (2¾ oz) of the beetroot and apple chutney on to each serving plate. Slice the pork and serve with the chutney and roasted parsnips then season. Store the remaining chutney in a lidded jar for up to 1 week.

Lamb pasta with rocket

ProPoints values per recipe 23

Takes 55 mins

4 large **shallots**, halved or quartered, if large
3 bay leaves
calorie controlled cooking spray
4 **tomatoes**, quartered
4 large **garlic cloves**, unpeeled
250 g (9 oz) lean lamb steaks, trimmed
    of all visible fat
110 g (4 oz) dried penne
30 g (1¼ oz) **rocket leaves**
salt and freshly ground black pepper

1 Preheat the oven to Gas Mark 6/200°C/ fan oven 180°C. Put the shallots and bay leaves in a non stick roasting tray, spray with the cooking spray and roast for 5 minutes. Add the tomatoes and garlic, spray again, and return to the oven for 20 minutes until tender.

2 Heat a non stick frying pan until hot. Spray the lamb with the cooking spray, season, and cook for 1–2 minutes on each side until evenly browned. Place on top of the vegetables then return to the oven for 12–15 minutes until cooked. Remove the tray from the oven and set aside the meat to rest for 5 minutes.

3 Meanwhile, bring a pan of water to the boil, add the pasta and cook according to the packet instructions. Drain, reserving 3 tablespoons of the cooking water.

4 Slice the lamb into 1 cm (½ inch) thick slices. Squeeze the garlic out of its papery shell and chop finely. Return the garlic to the roasting tray with the pasta, reserved cooking water, rocket and lamb. Toss until combined then season. Serve straightaway, pouring over any juices from the tray.

Chicken cacciatore

ProPoints values per recipe 14

25 mins prep, 20 mins cooking

calorie controlled cooking spray
285 g (10 oz) **skinless boneless chicken
    breasts**, cut into large bite size pieces
1 **onion**, sliced
40 g (1½ oz) lean back bacon, diced
2 **garlic cloves**, chopped
100 ml (3½ fl oz) white wine
400 g can chopped **tomatoes**
1 teaspoon tomato purée
1 bay leaf
1 tablespoon **fresh thyme leaves**, plus
    extra sprigs to garnish
90 g (3¼ oz) canned **cannellini beans**,
    drained and rinsed
1 tablespoon capers in brine, drained and rinsed
salt and freshly ground black pepper

1 Heat a large lidded casserole dish, spray with the cooking spray, add the chicken and sauté for 3 minutes until browned all over.

2 Add the onion to the casserole dish. Cook for 3 minutes until softened, stirring occasionally. Add the bacon and cook for 3 minutes until golden and crisp. Stir in the garlic and cook for another minute.

3 Add the wine and boil gently for about 5 minutes until reduced by three quarters.

4 Add the chopped tomatoes, tomato purée, bay leaf, thyme and 3 tablespoons of water. Bring to the boil then reduce the heat and stir in the beans and capers. Simmer, partially covered, for 20 minutes, stirring occasionally, until reduced and cooked through. Season to taste and serve garnished with thyme.

V **Try this** For a vegetarian alternative, omit the chicken and and bacon and increase the quantity of cannellini beans to a 400 g can, drained and rinsed. Prepare in the same way for 6 **ProPoints** values per serving.

Pink trout in oatmeal with hotslaw

ProPoints values per recipe 17

Takes 15 mins

1 **egg**
50 g (1¾ oz) fine **oatmeal**
2 x 140 g (5 oz) pink **trout fillets**
calorie controlled cooking spray
salt and freshly ground black pepper
lemon wedges, to serve

For the hotslaw
1 small **onion**, sliced thinly
75 g (2¾ oz) white or red **cabbage**, shredded finely
1 **carrot**, peeled and grated coarsely
20 g (¾ oz) Dijon mustard
juice of ½ a lemon
2 teaspoons tartare sauce

Oatmeal gives a delicious crisp coating to fish fillets, which only take a few minutes to grill. You could serve the trout with 100 g (3½ oz) new **potatoes** per person, for an additional 2 **ProPoints** values per serving.

1 Preheat the grill to high and line the grill pan with foil. Beat the egg in a wide, shallow bowl.

2 Spread the oatmeal over the base of a dinner plate then season. Dip one side of each trout fillet into the egg and then the oatmeal until evenly coated. Spray the coated side of the fish with the cooking spray then grill, oat side up first, for 5–6 minutes, turning once until golden on top.

3 Meanwhile, to make the hotslaw, heat a wok or non stick frying pan until hot, spray with the cooking spray and stir fry the onion for a minute. Add the cabbage and carrot and cook for another 2 minutes. Remove from the heat and stir in the mustard, lemon juice and tartare sauce then season to taste.

4 Serve each fillet accompanied by the hotslaw and a wedge of lemon.

Whether it's the two of you sharing a romantic dinner together, or you and a friend celebrating a special occasion, you'll find original and inspiring recipe ideas here to delight you every time.

Special occasions

Moroccan spiced salmon with mango salad

ProPoints values per recipe 13

Takes 25 mins

1 teaspoon ground cumin or whole cumin seeds
1 teaspoon ras-el-hanout
½ teaspoon paprika
1 teaspoon dried oregano
2 x 125 g (4½ oz) salmon fillets
calorie controlled cooking spray
salt and freshly ground black pepper
2 lime wedges, to serve

For the mango salad
25 g (1 oz) baby spinach leaves
25 g (1 oz) rocket leaves
½ small red onion, sliced thinly into rounds
100 g (3½ oz) fresh mango, cubed
1 tablespoon lime juice
1 tablespoon chopped fresh mint
1 tablespoon chopped fresh coriander

Ras-el-hanout is a North African spice blend that is readily available in major supermarkets. Serve the salmon with 100 g (3½ oz) new potatoes per person, for an additional 2 **ProPoints** values per serving.

1 To make the salad, arrange the spinach and rocket in a large, shallow bowl. Scatter over the onion and mango then sprinkle with the lime juice. Scatter with the fresh herbs, season and then set aside.

2 Mix together the spices and oregano on a plate then season. Press the top of each fillet into the spice mixture until evenly coated.

3 Heat a non stick frying pan, spray the fish with the cooking spray and place spice side down in the pan. Cook over a medium-low heat for 1 minute, or until the top is sealed, then turn over and cook for a further 6–8 minutes, depending on the thickness of the fillets. Serve the salmon with the mango salad and lime wedges on the side.

V **Try this** For a vegetarian alternative, pat dry 250 g (9 oz) tofu with paper towels. Cut into 1 cm (½ inch) thick slices and scatter over the spices. Spray with cooking spray and pan fry for 5 minutes on each side until golden. Serve on top of the mango salad for 4 **ProPoints** values per serving.

Turkey with vermouth and tarragon sauce

ProPoints values per recipe 13

15 mins prep, 25 mins cooking

calorie controlled cooking spray
2 x 150 g (5½ oz) **turkey breast steaks**
4 **shallots** or 1 small **onion**, sliced thinly
60 ml (2½ fl oz) vermouth or dry white wine
225 ml (8 fl oz) chicken or vegetable stock
2 teaspoons finely chopped **fresh tarragon**, plus 2 sprigs to garnish
150 g (5½ oz) fine **green beans**, trimmed
2 tablespoons half fat crème fraîche
salt and freshly ground black pepper

1 Heat a lidded non stick frying pan and spray with the cooking spray. Add the turkey steaks and cook over a high heat for about 2 minutes on each side until seared and browned. Add the shallots or onion.

2 Pour in the vermouth or white wine and allow it to bubble up for a few seconds. Add the stock and chopped tarragon and season. Partially cover and simmer over a very low heat for 20–25 minutes.

3 Just before the turkey is ready, bring a pan of water to the boil, add the beans and cook for 5 minutes then drain. When the turkey is ready, the juices will run clear when the thickest part is pierced with a sharp knife. Lift the steaks and beans on to two warmed serving plates and keep warm.

4 Cook the sauce until it has reduced down slightly, then remove from the heat and stir in the crème fraîche. Check the seasoning, then spoon over the turkey steaks and serve garnished with the tarragon sprigs and accompanied by the green beans.

Try this Serve the steaks with a root vegetable mash, such as a combination of **carrots**, **butternut squash** and **swede**, for no additional **ProPoints** values.

Chicken with orange and fennel salad

ProPoints values per recipe 8

Takes 30 mins

2 x 165 g (5¾ oz) **skinless boneless chicken breasts**
calorie controlled cooking spray
1 teaspoon finely chopped **fresh rosemary** or **fresh thyme**
salt and freshly ground black pepper

For the salad
1 large **orange**
1 small red **onion**, sliced thinly
1 small **fennel bulb**, sliced thinly
½ teaspoon cumin seeds, toasted
2 teaspoons red or white wine vinegar

1 Preheat the grill to a medium-high heat. Place the chicken between two pieces of cling film and bash to an even thickness. Spray with the cooking spray, season, then rub in the chopped rosemary or thyme.

2 Grill the chicken breasts for 12–15 minutes, turning occasionally, until thoroughly cooked. (Check by inserting a sharp knife into the chicken – the juices should run clear if it is cooked. If not, cook for a little longer.)

3 Meanwhile, prepare the salad. Using a sharp knife, remove all the peel and pith from the orange. Do this over a bowl to catch the juice, which is needed for the dressing. Cut the orange into segments, removing all the pith, and add to the bowl.

4 Add the onion, fennel, cumin seeds and vinegar to the oranges, tossing everything together gently to combine. Season, then pile on to two plates and serve with the hot chicken breasts, spooning the dressing over them.

Cook's tip To toast the cumin seeds, put them in a dry non stick frying pan and cook them over a medium heat for 1–2 minutes, stirring often. If you prefer, substitute some sliced **celery** or **carrot** for the red onion, for no additional **ProPoints** values.

Butternut squash, spinach and feta lasagne

ProPoints values per recipe 15

Takes 30 mins

450 g (1 lb) butternut squash, peeled,
    de-seeded and cut into 1 cm (½ inch) cubes

calorie controlled cooking spray

150 g (5½ oz) cherry or baby plum tomatoes,
    halved

225 g (8 oz) spinach leaves, washed

3 fresh egg lasagne sheets, measuring 20 x 15 cm
    (8 x 6 inches), cut in half

2 tablespoons red or green pesto sauce

75 g (2¾ oz) feta light

salt and freshly ground black pepper

fresh basil leaves, to garnish

1 Preheat the oven to Gas Mark 6/200°C/fan oven 180°C.

2 Put the butternut squash in a roasting pan and spray with the cooking spray, tossing to coat lightly. Roast for 20 minutes, or until the squash is just tender, then add the tomatoes and roast for 5 more minutes.

3 Meanwhile, cook the spinach in a small amount of water for 2–3 minutes, until the leaves have wilted. Drain well, squeezing out the excess moisture with the back of a spoon. At the same time, bring a large pan of water to the boil, add the lasagne and cook for 3–4 minutes.

4 Remove the squash and tomatoes from the oven. Stir the pesto sauce through them and season.

5 Drain the lasagne sheets well, and then layer them on to two warmed plates with the squash mixture and the spinach. Sprinkle the feta on top, drizzle over any remaining roasting juices, then serve garnished with the basil leaves.

Cook's tip To use dried lasagne sheets, cook them for a few minutes longer and then cut them in half once they are cooked.

Rich Hungarian beef goulash

ProPoints values per recipe 15

25 mins prep, 1½ hrs cooking

calorie controlled cooking spray
300 g (10½ oz) **lean braising steak**,
  cut into chunks
2 teaspoons paprika
1 **onion**, sliced
1 **garlic clove**, crushed
1 large **carrot**, peeled and sliced
1 red **pepper**, de-seeded and chopped
400 g can chopped **tomatoes**
150 ml (5 fl oz) beef stock
1 tablespoon cornflour
salt and freshly ground black pepper
20 g (¾ oz) low fat crème fraîche, to serve
chopped **fresh parsley**, to garnish

This goulash goes well with 100 g (3½ oz) boiled new **potatoes** but just remember to add the extra 2 **ProPoints** values per serving.

1 Heat a large non stick saucepan and spray with the cooking spray. Add the beef, a handful at a time, and cook for about 2–3 minutes over a high heat until sealed and browned.

2 Add the paprika, onion and garlic and cook, stirring, for 1–2 minutes, then add the carrot, pepper, tomatoes and stock. Cover and cook over a very low heat for 1½ hours, or until the meat is very tender. Check the liquid level occasionally, adding a little water if needed.

3 Blend the cornflour with 2 tablespoons of cold water, then add to the goulash and stir until thickened. Season to taste.

4 Serve the goulash with 2 teaspoons of crème fraîche per portion, garnished with the chopped parsley.

Cook's tip If you like your food spicy, add a little more paprika.

Try this Use the same weight of **skinless boneless chicken breasts** for 6 **ProPoints** values per serving but reduce the cooking time to 1 hour.

Pork with ginger rhubarb sauce

ProPoints values per recipe 15

Takes 30 mins + 30 mins marinating

2 teaspoons dark soy sauce
½ teaspoon Tabasco
1 tablespoon balsamic vinegar
2 x 150 g (5½ oz) **lean pork fillets**,
  trimmed of fat
calorie controlled cooking spray
salt and freshly ground black pepper

For the ginger rhubarb sauce
125 g (4½ oz) **rhubarb**, trimmed and cut
  into 2.5 cm (1 inch) pieces
2 tablespoons caster sugar
1 teaspoon ground ginger
2 x 1 cm (½ inch) thick slices **fresh
  root ginger**

Rhubarb complements pork perfectly and this delicious rhubarb sauce is given some extra zing with ginger. Serve with fine **green beans** for no additional **ProPoints** values.

1 Mix together the soy sauce, Tabasco and balsamic vinegar in a shallow dish. Add the pork and season, then spoon the marinade over until coated. Cover and leave to marinate in the fridge for 30 minutes.

2 Preheat the oven to Gas Mark 5/190°C/fan oven 170°C. Heat a non stick frying pan, spray the pork with the cooking spray and cook for 2 minutes on each side until browned. Place in a non stick baking tray, spoon over a little more of the marinade and roast for about 12 minutes until cooked through.

3 Meanwhile, make the sauce. Put the rhubarb in a lidded pan with 6 tablespoons of water, sugar and the ground and fresh ginger. Bring to the boil, stir, then reduce the heat to low. Cover and simmer for 10 minutes until the rhubarb is tender. Serve the pork with the sauce on the side.

Spanish cod with chorizo

ProPoints values per recipe 16

Takes 25 mins

50 g (1¾ oz) chorizo sausage, chopped into
    small chunks

2 x 175 g (6 oz) skinless chunky **cod** loin

6 **spring onions**, sliced finely

410 g can **cannellini beans** in water,
    drained and rinsed

100 ml (3½ fl oz) vegetable stock

zest and juice of ½ a lemon

6 cherry **tomatoes**, halved

1 **courgette**, chopped into small chunks

1 tablespoon chopped **fresh flat leaf parsley**,
    plus extra to garnish

freshly ground black pepper

2 bunches of cherry tomatoes on the vine, to garnish

1 Heat a large, lidded, non stick frying pan and add the chunks of chorizo, cooking over a medium heat so that the juices run. Add the cod and cook for 2 minutes on each side, then remove from the pan with a fish slice and set aside.

2 Add the spring onions to the frying pan and cook for 3–4 minutes, stirring, until softened.

3 Add the beans, vegetable stock, lemon zest, lemon juice, tomatoes and courgette to the pan. Stir in the parsley and season with black pepper.

4 Return the cod to the frying pan and cover with the lid or a piece of foil. Cook over a low heat for 6–8 minutes so that the cod steams. When cooked, the fish should be opaque and flake easily with a fork.

5 Serve at once, garnished with the parsley and tomatoes on the vine.

Cook's tip Look for chorizo sausages in the chilled cabinet or the deli section of your local supermarket. If you have to buy more than you need, freeze in 50 g (1¾ oz) batches, cut into small chunks, so you can make this recipe again.

Try this If you prefer, you could use a 410 g can of **mixed pulses** instead of the cannellini beans, for 9 **ProPoints** values per serving.

Pepper, courgette, aubergine and ricotta bake

ProPoints values per recipe 8

25 mins prep + 20 mins cooling, 30 mins cooking

calorie controlled cooking spray
1 courgette, sliced lengthways
1 small aubergine, sliced lengthways
200 g (7 oz) roasted red peppers in brine, drained
2 eggs
100 g (3½ oz) ricotta cheese
6 tablespoons vegetable stock
2 teaspoons chopped fresh thyme
salt and freshly ground black pepper

This is an excellent recipe to enjoy in the summer, when all these delicious vegetables are in season.

1. Preheat the oven to Gas Mark 4/180°C/fan oven 160°C. Spray an 18 cm (7 inch) round, loose-based, cake tin with the cooking spray.

2. Preheat the grill to medium. Spray the courgette and aubergine slices with the cooking spray, then grill for a few minutes on each side until tender. You'll need to do this in batches.

3. Place a layer of roasted red peppers in the base of the cake tin, then arrange a layer of courgettes on top. Continue with a layer of aubergines, then repeat the layers once more.

4. Beat the eggs with the ricotta cheese, stock and thyme. Season and pour into the cake tin.

5. Stand the cake tin on a baking tray and bake for 25–30 minutes. Cool in the tin for 15–20 minutes, then carefully turn it out. Slice and serve warm or cold.

Try this Cut into four wedges to serve as a starter for four, garnished with rocket or fresh herbs, for 2 **ProPoints** values per serving.

Special occasions

Chicken with mushroom and Marsala sauce

ProPoints values per recipe 11

25 mins prep, 20 mins cooking

2 x 165 g (5¾ oz) **skinless boneless chicken breasts**
4 **fresh sage leaves**
calorie controlled cooking spray
4 tablespoons Marsala or medium sherry
100 g (3½ oz) **mushrooms**, sliced
225 ml (8 fl oz) chicken or vegetable stock
freshly ground black pepper

1 Using a sharp knife, cut a pocket into each chicken breast. Stuff two sage leaves into each pocket. Close the pockets and secure with cocktail sticks.

2 Heat a non stick frying pan and spray with the cooking spray. Add the chicken breasts and cook on each side for 2–3 minutes, until seared and lightly browned.

3 Pour in the Marsala or sherry and allow it to bubble up for a few seconds. Add the mushrooms and stock, then season with black pepper. Partially cover the pan and simmer over a low heat for 20 minutes, turning the chicken after 10 minutes.

4 Check that the chicken is cooked by piercing the thickest part with a sharp knife – the juices should run clear. If there is any trace of pink, cook for a few more minutes.

5 Serve the chicken and mushrooms with the sauce poured over.

Try this Use two 150 g (5½ oz) **turkey breast steaks** instead of chicken for 5 **ProPoints** values per serving.

Chicken, porcini mushroom and sage risotto

ProPoints values per recipe 22

Takes 35 mins + 30 mins soaking

250 ml (9 fl oz) boiling water
25 g (1 oz) dried porcini mushrooms
calorie controlled cooking spray
125 g (4½ oz) dried risotto rice
60 ml (2½ fl oz) dry white wine
200 g (7 oz) **skinless boneless chicken breasts**, chopped into 2 cm (¾ inch) pieces
1 **garlic clove**, crushed
1 small **leek**, sliced thinly
2–3 **fresh sage leaves**
600 ml (20 fl oz) hot vegetable stock
25 g (1 oz) frozen **peas**, thawed
10 g (¼ oz) Parmesan cheese, grated finely
freshly ground black pepper

1 Pour the boiling water over the porcini mushrooms and leave to soak for at least 30 minutes.

2 Spray a large non stick frying pan or saucepan with the cooking spray. Add the rice and cook over a low heat for 1–2 minutes, stirring all the time, until the rice looks glossy, but not brown.

3 Add the white wine to the pan and let it bubble for a few moments, then add the chicken, garlic, leek and sage leaves. Pour in the soaked mushrooms along with their liquid, then add a ladleful of stock. Stir well.

4 Cook over a medium heat for 20–25 minutes, stirring often, and gradually add the remaining stock, until the rice has absorbed all the liquid and has a nice creamy texture. If necessary, add a little extra stock or water.

5 Add the peas, stirring gently to mix them in. Check the seasoning, then share the risotto between two warm plates or bowls. Sprinkle each portion with 1 teaspoon of Parmesan cheese and serve.

Ⓥ Try this You could omit the chicken to make a vegetarian risotto if you prefer, for 9 **ProPoints** values per portion.

Spaghetti vongole

ProPoints values per recipe 22

Takes 30 mins

A real treat, this dish is made with fresh clams but, if they are out of season, you could use 200 g (7 oz) canned clams.

575 g (1 lb 4 oz) **fresh clams**
125 g (4½ oz) dried spaghetti
2 teaspoons olive oil
3 **garlic cloves**, chopped finely
3 **tomatoes**, de-seeded and diced
½ red **chilli**, de-seeded and chopped finely
2 tablespoons chopped **fresh parsley**
150 ml (5 fl oz) dry white wine
freshly ground black pepper

1 If you are using clams in shells, discard any clams with broken shells and those that remain open when tapped. Rinse the clams in plenty of cold running water.

2 Bring a saucepan of water to the boil, add the pasta and cook, following the packet instructions, until al dente. Drain.

3 Meanwhile, heat the olive oil in a large, lidded, deep sided sauté or non stick frying pan. Cook the garlic, tomatoes, chilli and half the parsley for 1–2 minutes then pour in the wine and boil gently for 2 minutes.

4 Add the clams to the pan, cover, and cook for 4–5 minutes, shaking the pan occasionally until the clams open. Discard any that haven't opened. Remove the clam meat from most of the shells, reserving a few shells to garnish with.

5 Toss the pasta into the pan and season with black pepper. Serve immediately, sprinkled with the remaining parsley.

Roast red pork with lemon rice

ProPoints values per recipe 27

35 mins prep + 8 hrs marinating,
25 mins cooking

275 g (9½ oz) **lean pork fillet**, in one piece,
    trimmed
3 **garlic cloves**, crushed
2 teaspoons finely grated **fresh root ginger**
30 g (1¼ oz) Thai red curry paste
1 tablespoon soy sauce
2 teaspoons dark muscovado sugar
1 teaspoon toasted sesame oil
calorie controlled cooking spray
2 **shallots** or 1 small **onion**, chopped finely
120 g (4½ oz) dried basmati rice
1 strip of lemon zest
3 cardamom pods, split
4 cloves
300 ml (10 fl oz) vegetable stock
fresh coriander sprigs, to garnish

1　Put the pork into a large plastic food bag or freezer bag. Add two garlic cloves, the ginger, curry paste, soy sauce, sugar and sesame oil. Roll the mixture around to coat the pork, then secure the opening. Chill for at least 8 hours or overnight.

2　Preheat the oven to Gas Mark 4/180°C/fan oven 160°C. Line a small roasting tin with foil, then put the pork in it. Roast, uncovered, towards the top of the oven for 15 minutes.

3　Meanwhile, spray a small, lidded, flameproof casserole dish, with a tight fitting lid, with the cooking spray. Add the shallots or onion and remaining garlic. Sauté over a low heat for about 3 minutes until soft, but not brown.

4　Remove from the heat and add the rice, lemon zest, cardamom pods, cloves and vegetable stock. Stir well, then cover with the lid. Transfer to the oven and bake below the pork for exactly 25 minutes (this timing is important for the best result), without removing the lid.

5　Remove the pork from the oven, cover with foil and leave to rest for 5 minutes before slicing. At the same time, remove the casserole dish from the oven and allow it to stand for 5 minutes, without removing the lid.

6　Slice the pork and serve with the rice. Garnish with the coriander sprigs.

Gnocchi and courgette bakes

ProPoints values per recipe 22

20 mins prep, 30 mins cooking

calorie controlled cooking spray
200 g (7 oz) fresh gnocchi
75 g (2¾ oz) baby **plum tomatoes**, halved
1 **courgette**, grated
2 tablespoons red or green pesto sauce
6–8 **fresh basil leaves**, torn into shreds,
    plus a few to garnish
2 **eggs**
100 g (3½ oz) low fat soft cheese
freshly ground black pepper
20 g (¾ oz) Parmesan cheese, grated finely

1　Preheat the oven to Gas Mark 5/190°C/fan oven 170°C. Spray two 20 x 12 cm (8 x 4½ inch) shallow ovenproof dishes with the cooking spray.

2　Bring a pan of water to the boil, add the gnocchi and cook according to the packet instructions. Drain well, return to the saucepan and add the tomatoes, courgette, pesto sauce and torn basil leaves, stirring gently to combine. Share the gnocchi between the prepared dishes.

3　Beat together the eggs and soft cheese. Season with black pepper and pour into the dishes. Sprinkle each dish with half of the Parmesan cheese.

4　Stand the dishes on a baking tray and transfer to the middle shelf of the oven. Bake for 25–30 minutes until set and golden brown. Serve garnished with a few basil leaves.

Cook's tip You can use pre-packed gnocchi, sold in 400–500 g bags. Once the packet is opened, the gnocchi will keep in the refrigerator for up to 4 days. Otherwise, freeze the gnocchi and use within 2 months, allowing it to defrost for 2–3 hours before use.

Pork with apple and potato dauphinoise

ProPoints values per recipe 20

Takes 45 mins

200 g (7 oz) **potatoes**, peeled and sliced
    crossways thinly
1 **onion**, sliced crossways thinly
1 large **garlic clove**, sliced thinly
1 **fresh rosemary** sprig
1 bay leaf
200 ml (7 fl oz) skimmed milk
1 **apple**, peeled, cored and sliced
    crossways thinly
2 tablespoons low fat soft cheese
1 teaspoon wholegrain mustard
calorie controlled cooking spray
2 x 150 g (5½ oz) **lean pork
    medallions** or **fillets**
salt and freshly ground black pepper

Serve with **broccoli** florets and **leeks** for no additional **ProPoints** values.

1 Put the potatoes, onion, garlic, rosemary and bay leaf in a pan. Pour over the milk and cook on a low heat for 12–15 minutes until the potatoes are tender.

2 Meanwhile, cook the apple in a little water for 6–8 minutes until tender then drain.

3 Preheat the grill to high. Take a sheet of foil large enough to hold the pork then turn up the sides to make a tray.

4 Strain the potato mixture, reserving the cooking liquid and discard the herbs. Arrange half of the potatoes and onions in an even layer in a small ovenproof dish, top with the apple and then with the rest of the potatoes and onions. Mix the soft cheese and mustard into the cooking liquid, season and pour it over the dauphinoise.

5 Spray and season both sides of the pork then put it in the foil tray and grill for 12 minutes, or until cooked through, turning once. After 2 minutes, place the dauphinoise under the grill next to the pork and cook until the top is golden.

6 Serve the pork, drizzled with some of the juices from the foil, and the dauphinoise potatoes by the side.

Steak with blue cheese cream

ProPoints values per recipe 13

Takes 20 mins + 30 mins softening

2 x 125 g (4 ½ oz) **beef fillet steaks**,
    trimmed of visible fat
2 teaspoons snipped **fresh chives**
salt and freshly ground black pepper

For the blue cheese cream
25 g (1 oz) rindless Stilton cheese
2 tablespoons **0% fat Greek yogurt**
1 teaspoon half fat crème fraîche

For the caramelised tomatoes
calorie controlled cooking spray
175 g (6 oz) **cherry tomatoes** on the vine
1 tablespoon balsamic vinegar

Chips are a must with steak. For two people, cut 300 g (10½ oz) unpeeled **potatoes** into wedges, spray with cooking spray and roast for 45 minutes, turning once, until crisp, for an extra 3 **ProPoints** values per serving.

1 To make the blue cheese cream, remove the Stilton from the fridge at least 30 minutes before use to soften. In a bowl, mash it with the back of a fork then add the yogurt and crème fraîche. Season with black pepper and beat with a wooden spoon until smooth and creamy. Set aside.

2 Heat a large non stick frying pan. Spray the tomatoes with the cooking spray then cook, turning once, for 1 minute. Pour in the balsamic vinegar and cook for 2 more minutes, turning occasionally, until the tomatoes start to caramelise and soften. Season, remove from the pan and keep warm.

3 Wipe the pan clean and return to a medium-high heat. Spray the steaks with the cooking spray, season, and cook for 2–3 minutes on each side or until cooked to your liking.

4 Serve the steaks with a spoonful of the blue cheese cream, sprinkled with the chives, and the tomatoes on the side.

Lamb with olives and flame roasted peppers

ProPoints values per recipe 20

Takes 30 mins

2 x 125 g (4½ oz) lean lamb steaks, trimmed
of visible fat
calorie controlled cooking spray
1 onion, sliced
100 g (3½ oz) fennel, sliced into wedges
(reserve and chop the green fronds, to garnish)
2 garlic cloves, sliced thinly
200 ml (7 fl oz) dry white wine
4 fresh thyme sprigs
200 ml (7 fl oz) vegetable stock
50 g (1¾ oz) green olives in brine
100 g (3½ oz) flame roasted red peppers
in a jar, drained and torn into pieces
salt and freshly ground black pepper

1 Heat a deep, lidded, non stick frying pan. Spray the lamb steaks with the cooking spray and season. Cook the lamb for 2 minutes on each side until browned then remove, cover, and set aside.

2 Add the onion and fennel to the pan, spray with the cooking spray, and sauté for 5 minutes until softened. Stir in the garlic and cook for a minute before pouring in the wine and adding the thyme sprigs. Allow the wine to bubble and reduce for about 5 minutes.

3 Add the stock, olives and peppers and bring to the boil. Reduce the heat and simmer, partially covered, for 5 minutes. Return the lamb to the pan, spoon the juices over the top, cover, and simmer for another 5 minutes until the meat is tender and the vegetables are cooked. Season and serve garnished with the fennel fronds.

Try this Soak up the juices with some delicious mashed potato. For two people, cook 200 g (7 oz) peeled, cubed potatoes for 10 minutes or until tender. Drain and mash with 2 tablespoons of extra light mayonnaise and 50 ml (2 fl oz) skimmed milk until creamy. Season before serving. This adds an extra 3 **ProPoints** values per serving.

Cook's tip Flame roasted red peppers can be bought in jars and will keep in the fridge for a couple of weeks after opening. They're also used in the Courgette, Pesto and Feta Crostini (see page 11).

These divine desserts make the perfect end to an enjoyable meal. Most of them are so quick and easy, you won't even think twice about whether or not you both want a little something extra.

Delightful desserts

Cappuccino sponge puddings

ProPoints values per recipe 11

15 mins prep + cooling, 18 mins baking

calorie controlled cooking spray
2 teaspoons instant coffee granules
2–3 drops vanilla extract
2 tablespoons skimmed milk
1 large egg
25 g (1 oz) light or dark muscovado sugar
25 g (1 oz) plain flour
2 tablespoons half fat crème fraîche
½ teaspoon cocoa powder

Baking these delicious coffee flavoured puddings in teacups makes them look very special but ramekin dishes work well too.

1 Preheat the oven to Gas Mark 4/180°C/fan oven 160°C. Spray two ovenproof teacups or ramekin dishes, with a capacity of at least 150 ml (5 fl oz), with the cooking spray.

2 Heat the milk gently and then mix the coffee granules and vanilla extract into the hot milk. Allow to cool.

3 Using a hand held mixer, whisk the egg and sugar together until very light and fluffy. This will take about 3–4 minutes on a high speed. Fold in the flour using a large metal spoon, then gently stir in the coffee flavoured milk.

4 Share the mixture between the cups or ramekin dishes, then stand them in a roasting tin and add enough hot water to come about one third of the way up their sides.

5 Bake for 15–18 minutes. Remove from the oven and cool for a few minutes.

6 Share the crème fraîche between the puddings and serve, sprinkled with cocoa powder.

Try this Make chocolate sponge puddings by blending 2 teaspoons of unsweetened cocoa powder with the hot milk instead of the instant coffee, for the same *ProPoints* values per serving.

Peach and almond puff tarts

ProPoints values per recipe 9

15 mins prep + 10 mins cooling, 20 mins baking

calorie controlled cooking spray
1 teaspoon plain flour
50 g (1¾ oz) puff pastry, defrosted if frozen
1 teaspoon vanilla extract
2 teaspoons lemon juice
1 small ripe **peach**, pitted and sliced thinly
2 teaspoons caster sugar

To serve
5 g (¼ oz) toasted flaked almonds
¼ teaspoon icing sugar

1 Preheat the oven to Gas Mark 6/200°C/fan oven 180°C. Spray a baking sheet with the cooking spray.

2 Use the flour to dust a work surface, then roll out the puff pastry on it. Use a 9 cm (3½ inch) cutter to stamp out two circles. Lift them on to the baking sheets.

3 Put the vanilla extract and lemon juice in a bowl. Add the peach slices and toss in the lemon juice mixture. Arrange on top of the pastry circles.

4 Transfer to the oven and bake for 15–20 minutes, until the pastry is golden brown. Cool for about 10 minutes.

5 Put the sugar in a saucepan with 2 tablespoons of cold water. Simmer over a low heat until the sugar has dissolved and the mixture is syrupy. Brush the mixture over the tarts to glaze them. Serve, sprinkled with the almonds, and a little icing sugar.

Cook's tip You can freeze the tarts for up to 2 months in a freezer box or bag. Allow 1 hour for them to defrost and then warm them in the oven for 5–8 minutes at Gas Mark 3/160°C/fan oven 140°C before serving.

Pear and mincemeat strudel

ProPoints values per recipe 13

25 mins prep, 30 mins baking

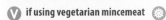 if using vegetarian mincemeat

calorie controlled cooking spray
2 x 45 g (1½ oz) filo pastry sheets, measuring
    50 x 24 cm (20 x 9½ inches), and defrosted
    if frozen
2 conference **pears**, peeled, cored and
    sliced thinly
30 g (1¼ oz) mincemeat
finely grated zest and juice of ½ a lemon
a pinch of ground cinnamon
1 teaspoon icing sugar
2 tablespoons low fat crème fraîche

This elegant dessert is ideal for the Christmas season.

1 Preheat the oven to Gas Mark 5/190°C/fan oven 170°C. Spray a baking sheet with the cooking spray.

2 Cut the filo pastry sheets in half lengthways. Put two pieces on top of each other on a work surface. Spray with the cooking spray.

3 In a bowl, toss together the sliced pears, the mincemeat, lemon zest, lemon juice and cinnamon, then scatter half of the mixture evenly over the pastry. Repeat the layers of pastry, the cooking spray and pear mixture once more.

4 Carefully roll up the filo pastry from the short end. It will be a little tricky, so use a fish slice to help you, and slide the baking sheet underneath. Don't worry if the pastry breaks a little. Spray with the cooking spray.

5 Bake for 25–30 minutes until golden then cool briefly.

6 Sprinkle with the icing sugar and serve warm, with 1 tablespoon of low fat crème fraîche each.

Cook's tip You can prepare this ahead of time and then warm the strudel at Gas Mark 3/160°C/fan oven 140°C for 10 minutes before serving.

Strawberry soufflé omelettes

ProPoints values per recipe 4

Takes 20 mins

1 **orange**
200 g (7 oz) **strawberries**, halved
100 g (3½ oz) **blueberries**
4 **egg whites**
15 g (½ oz) caster sugar
½ teaspoon vanilla extract
calorie controlled cooking spray
2 teaspoons icing sugar

1 Finely grate ½ a teaspoon of zest from the orange and reserve for later, then use a sharp, serrated knife to remove all the peel and pith. Do this over a saucepan to catch the juice. Cut the orange into segments and add to the saucepan with the strawberries, blueberries and 2 tablespoons of water. Heat very gently and keep warm over a low heat.

2 Using a hand held whisk, whip the egg whites in a large grease-free bowl until they hold their shape. Gradually add the sugar, whisking well until the egg whites are stiff and glossy. Whisk in the vanilla extract and orange zest.

3 Preheat the grill to high. Heat a non stick frying pan on the hob and spray with the cooking spray. Add half of the whisked egg white, spreading it to cover the surface of the pan, and cook over a low heat until the base has set – about 2 minutes. Transfer to the grill to set the surface.

4 Fill with the warm fruit mixture and slide the omelette on to a warmed plate. Cook the second one in the same way. Dust with icing sugar and serve.

Try this Use 300 g (10½ oz) defrosted frozen **forest fruits** instead of fresh strawberries and blueberries, for the same **ProPoints** values per serving.

Pineapple and banana muscovado melts

ProPoints values per recipe 6

Takes 10 mins

200 g (7 oz) fresh **pineapple** pieces
1 **banana**, sliced
100 g (3½ oz) low fat soft cheese
125 g (4½ oz) **low fat plain yogurt**
2–3 drops vanilla extract
a pinch of mixed spice
2 teaspoons dark or light muscovado sugar

In this fruity, refreshing dessert, the muscovado sugar melts within a matter of minutes to create a lovely toffee-like sauce.

1 Combine the pineapple and banana and share equally between two serving glasses.

2 Put the soft cheese into a bowl and beat for a few moments with a wooden spoon until creamy. Add the yogurt, vanilla and mixed spice and beat until smooth. Spoon an equal amount on top of each portion of fruit.

3 Sprinkle 1 teaspoon of muscovado sugar on to each dessert and wait a few minutes for it to melt before serving.

Cook's tips Fresh pre-packed pineapple pieces are readily available in supermarkets these days, so you don't have to buy a whole pineapple.

Prepare the desserts shortly before serving them, otherwise the banana will start to go brown.

Try this You could use **canned pineapple in natural juice**, drained, instead of fresh, for the same **ProPoints** values.

Nectarines with lemon and amaretti cream

ProPoints values per recipe 9

Takes 15 mins

2 ripe **nectarines**, halved and pitted
100 g (3½ oz) **blueberries**
2 teaspoons caster sugar
2 tablespoons Disaronno amaretto liqueur
    or Marsala
75 g (2¾ oz) low fat soft cheese
½ teaspoon finely grated lemon zest
25 g (1 oz) amaretti or ratafia biscuits, crushed

With its Italian inspired flavours, this easy dessert tastes sensational.

1 Preheat the grill to high. Take a tiny slice from the base of each nectarine half, so that they sit steadily on a baking sheet, cut sides up. Grill for 3–4 minutes.

2 Meanwhile, put the blueberries in a small saucepan with the sugar, 1 tablespoon of water and the liqueur or Marsala. Cook gently for about 2–3 minutes, until the fruit has softened.

3 Mix together the soft cheese, lemon zest and crushed biscuits. Spoon into the cavities of the nectarines and grill for a further 30–40 seconds.

4 Lift the nectarines into two bowls, then spoon the warm blueberries on top. Serve at once.

Try this Use a sweet sherry instead of the Disaronno or Marsala. For a non alcoholic version, substitute the same amount of fruit juice – orange or mango juice would work well. The **ProPoints** values would be 3 per serving.

Forest fruit flummery

ProPoints values per recipe 5

Takes 15 mins + chilling

125 g (4½ oz) frozen **forest fruits**, thawed
125 g (4½ oz) low fat forest fruit yogurt
50 g (1¾ oz) low fat soft cheese
½ teaspoon finely grated lemon zest
1 **egg white**
2 teaspoons caster sugar
fresh mint leaves, to decorate

This lovely, light dessert can be put together in minutes – and enjoyed as a delightful finale to your meal.

1 Using a hand held blender or liquidiser, blend the fruit, yogurt, soft cheese and lemon zest together.

2 In a clean, grease-free bowl and using a hand held electric whisk, whisk the egg white until it holds its shape. Add the caster sugar and whisk again for a few seconds.

3 Use a metal spoon to fold the egg white into the fruit mixture until fully incorporated. Share between two serving glasses, then chill until ready to serve.

4 Serve the desserts decorated with the mint leaves.

Cook's tip Always make sure that the bowl and beaters are scrupulously clean when whisking egg whites, as any trace of grease will prevent them from whipping.

Try this Use frozen **raspberries** and low fat raspberry yogurt instead of forest fruits, for the same **ProPoints** values per serving.

Plum brûlées

ProPoints values per recipe 9

Takes 15 mins + cooling

6 **plums**, halved and pitted
finely grated zest and juice of 1 orange
30 ml (1 fl oz) brandy
a pinch of ground mixed spice
15 g (½ oz) dark or light muscovado sugar
6 tablespoons 0% fat Greek yogurt
2 teaspoons demerara sugar

1. Put the plums in a saucepan with the orange juice, half of the orange zest, the brandy, mixed spice and muscovado sugar. Heat and simmer gently for 6–8 minutes, until the plums are tender then leave to cool.

2. Share the plums between two heatproof serving dishes, such as large ramekin dishes.

3. Preheat the grill to high. Spoon the yogurt over the plums then sprinkle the remaining orange zest and 1 teaspoon of demerara sugar over each portion.

4. Grill until the sugar melts and bubbles. Cool briefly, then serve.

Cook's tip If you want to prepare ahead, keep the cooked plums and yogurt mixture separate in the fridge, then assemble and grill shortly before you want to eat.

Try this Omit the brandy for a non alcoholic version and use the juice from a large orange, for 3 **ProPoints** values per serving.

Apple and sultana crumble cakes

ProPoints values per recipe 11

20 mins prep + 10 mins cooling, 25 mins baking

calorie controlled cooking spray
40 g (1½ oz) wholemeal self raising flour
15 g (½ oz) porridge oats
a pinch of salt
15 g (½ oz) low fat spread
15 g (½ oz) light muscovado sugar
a pinch of ground mixed spice or ground cinnamon
1 small red eating apple, cored
    and sliced thinly
2 teaspoons lemon juice
15 g (½ oz) sultanas
2 teaspoons demerara sugar

This oaty bake can be served warm as a pudding or cold as a cake. Served either way, there will hardly be a crumb left.

1 Position an oven shelf in the centre of the oven. Preheat the oven to Gas Mark 4/180°C/fan oven 160°C. Spray two 7 cm (2¾ inch) metal cooking rings or two ramekin dishes with the cooking spray. Place on a baking sheet.

2 Mix together the flour, porridge oats and salt, then use your fingertips to rub in the low fat spread until the mixture resembles fine crumbs. Stir in the muscovado sugar and spice.

3 Tip half of the mixture into the prepared rings or ramekins and press it down lightly. Toss the apple slices in lemon juice, then arrange half of them in the rings or ramekins and sprinkle the sultanas on top. Spoon the remaining crumble mixture over them, press down lightly, then arrange the remaining apple slices on top. Sprinkle 1 teaspoon of demerara sugar over each one.

4 Bake for 25 minutes until firm and golden brown. Cool for 5–10 minutes, then remove from the cooking rings or serve in the ramekins.

✳ **Cook's tip** Freeze in the cooking rings or ramekins, sealed in freezer bags, and use within 3 months. Defrost at room temperature for 2 hours.

Try this When blackberries are in season, use 40 g (1½ oz) instead of the sultanas. The *ProPoints* values will remain the same.

Hot rum punch papaya

ProPoints values per recipe 5

Takes 15 mins

1 large ripe papaya, halved and de-seeded
30 ml (1 fl oz) dark or light rum
finely grated zest and juice of ½ a lime
100 g (3½ oz) strawberries, halved
10 seedless red or green grapes, halved
1 passion fruit
20 g (¾ oz) demerara sugar

This easy fruit dessert comes packed with a punch.

1 Preheat the grill to hot. Put the papaya halves, cut side up, on to the grill pan and sprinkle with the rum, lime zest and juice.

2 Mix together the strawberries and grapes, then scoop in the seeds and pulp from the passion fruit. Pile this mixture into the papaya halves. Sprinkle 2 teaspoons of demerara sugar over each one.

3 Grill until the sugar melts and begins to bubble. Allow the fruit to cool for a few minutes, then serve while still warm.

Cook's tip Choose a papaya with a yellow skin to make sure it's ripe and full of flavour. Cut a tiny slice from the base of each half so they stand well.

Try this Replace the rum with the same amount of unsweetened orange juice for only 1 *ProPoints* value per serving.

ProPoints value index

Light meals

4 *ProPoints* values and under

courgette, pesto and feta crostini | 11
Parma ham and pear salad | 14

5 *ProPoints* values and under

Spanish egg gratin | 12

6 *ProPoints* values and under

eggs Arnold Bennett | 10

7 *ProPoints* values and under

crispy bacon and bean sauté | 17

8 *ProPoints* values and under

prawn and crab soup | 8
sweet chilli turkey balls with sweetcorn
    salsa | 13

9 *ProPoints* values and under

Quorn toasties | 16
seared chicken with mint yogurt dressing | 14

10 *ProPoints* values and under

Italian beef burgers | 16
lamb, spinach and pasta soup | 8

11 *ProPoints* values and under

spicy fishcakes | 10
steak sandwich with mushroom sauce | 7

12 *ProPoints* values and under

jacket potato with spicy lamb Bolognese | 12

Simple dinners

5 *ProPoints* values and under

Cantonese orange duck | 22
Japanese pork with chilli glaze | 19

6 *ProPoints* values and under

chilli chicken | 28
herb rubbed steak with squash mash | 24
sausage and pear hot pot | 32
slow cooked Asian beef stew | 22

7 *ProPoints* values and under

chicken cacciatore | 36
garlic, mushroom and Quorn pies | 20

8 *ProPoints* values and under

vegetable pilaf with spiced cashews | 26

---

winter ratatouille | 20

9 *ProPoints* values and under

pasta with feta and mint | 24
penne pasta with prawns and basil | 31
pink trout in oatmeal with hotslaw | 36
pork with quick beetroot and apple
    chutney | 34
quick lamb and chick pea hot pot | 27
summer white bean and vegetable stew | 32

10 *ProPoints* values and under

spiced lentils with lamb | 30

11 *ProPoints* values and under

lamb pasta with rocket | 34

12 *ProPoints* values and under

beef and vegetable noodle bowl | 30

14 *ProPoints* values and under

one pot Moroccan chicken | 28

Special occasions

4 *ProPoints* values and under

chicken with orange and fennel salad | 40
pepper, courgette, aubergine and ricotta
    bake | 45

6 *ProPoints* values and under

chicken with mushroom and
    Marsala sauce | 46
Moroccan spiced salmon with
    mango salad | 39

7 *ProPoints* values and under

pork with ginger rhubarb sauce | 42
rich Hungarian beef goulash | 42
steak with blue cheese cream | 50
turkey with vermouth and tarragon sauce | 40

8 *ProPoints* values and under

butternut squash, spinach and feta
    lasagne | 41
Spanish cod with chorizo | 44

10 *ProPoints* values and under

lamb with olives and flame roasted
    peppers | 51

---

pork with apple and potato dauphinoise | 50

11 *ProPoints* values and under

chicken, porcini mushroom and
    sage risotto | 46
gnocchi and courgette bakes | 48
spaghetti vongole | 47

14 *ProPoints* values and under

roast red pork with lemon rice | 48

Delightful desserts

2 *ProPoints* values and under

hot rum punch papaya | 60
strawberry soufflé omelettes | 56

3 *ProPoints* values and under

forest fruit flummery | 58
pineapple and banana muscovado melts | 56

4 *ProPoints* values and under

peach and almond puff tarts | 54
plum brûlées | 59

5 *ProPoints* values and under

apple and sultana crumble cakes | 60
nectarines with lemon and amaretti
    cream | 58

6 *ProPoints* values and under

cappuccino sponge puddings | 53
pear and mincemeat strudel | 54